LEARNING TARGETS
for Numeracy

Shape, Space and Measures

Key Stage 1

Wendy Clemson
David Clemson

Stanley Thornes (Publishers) Ltd

Stanley Thornes for TEACHERS:
BLUEPRINTS • PRIMARY COLOURS • LEARNING TARGETS

Stanley Thornes for Teachers publishes practical teacher's ideas books and photocopiable resources for use in primary schools. Our three key series, **Blueprints**, **Primary Colours** and **Learning Targets** together provide busy teachers with unbeatable curriculum coverage, inspiration and value for money. We mail teachers and schools about our books regularly. To join the mailing list simply photocopy and complete the form below and return using the **FREEPOST** address to receive regular updates on our new and existing titles. You may also like to add the name of a friend who would be interested in being on the mailing list. Books can be bought by credit card over the telephone and information obtained on (01242) 267280.

Please add my name to the *Stanley Thornes for* **TEACHERS** mailing list.

Mr/Mrs/Miss/Ms _____

Address _____

_____ postcode _____

School address _____

_____ postcode _____

Please also send information about *Stanley Thornes for* **TEACHERS** to:

Mr/Mrs/Miss/Ms _____

Address _____

_____ postcode _____

To: Marketing Services Dept., Stanley Thornes Ltd, FREEPOST (GR 782), Cheltenham, GL50 1BR

First published in 1999 by
Stanley Thornes Publishers Ltd
Ellenborough House
Wellington Street
Cheltenham GL50 1YW

99 00 01 02 03 / 10 9 8 7 6 5 4 3 2 1

A catalogue record for this book is available from the British Library.

ISBN 0-7487-3587-9

Printed and bound in Great Britain by Redwood Books, Trowbridge, Wiltshire.

CONTENTS

Welcome to
LEARNING TARGETS

Learning Targets is a series of practical teacher's resource books written to help you to plan and deliver well-structured, professional lessons in line with all the relevant curriculum documents.

Each Learning Target book provides exceptionally clear lesson plans that cover the whole of its stated curriculum plus a large bank of carefully structured copymasters. Links to the key curriculum documents are provided throughout to enable you to plan effectively.

The Learning Targets series has been written in response to the challenge confronting teachers not just to come up with teaching ideas that cover the curriculum but to ensure that they deliver high quality lessons every lesson with the emphasis on raising standards of pupil achievement.

The recent thinking from OFSTED, and the National Literacy and Numeracy Strategies on the key factors in effective teaching has been built into the structure of Learning Targets. These might be briefly summarised as follows:

➤➤ that effective teaching is active teaching directed to very clear objectives

➤➤ that good lessons are delivered with pace, rigour and purpose

➤➤ that good teaching requires a range of strategies – including interactive whole class sessions

➤➤ that ongoing formative assessment is essential to plan children's learning

➤➤ that differentiation is necessary but that it must be realistic.

The emphasis in Learning Targets is on absolute clarity. We have written and designed the books to enable you to access and deliver effective lessons as easily as possible, with the following aims:

➤➤ to plan and deliver rigorous, well-structured lessons

➤➤ to set explicit targets for achievement in every lesson that you teach

➤➤ to make the children aware of what they are going to learn

➤➤ to put the emphasis on direct, active teaching every time

➤➤ to make effective use of time and resources

➤➤ to employ the full range of recommended strategies whole-class, group and individual work

➤➤ to differentiate for ability groups realistically

➤➤ to use ongoing formative assessment to plan your next step

➤➤ to have ready access to usable pupil copymasters to support your teaching.

The page opposite provides an at-a-glance guide to the key features of the Learning Targets lessons and explains how they will enable you deliver effective lessons. The key to symbols on the lesson plans is set out here. ➤➤

How to deliver structured lessons with pace, rigour and purpose

Explicit targets for achievement in every lesson

The concise subject knowledge you need

Crystal clear lesson plan layouts

The full range of teaching strategies

Rigorous and practical activities

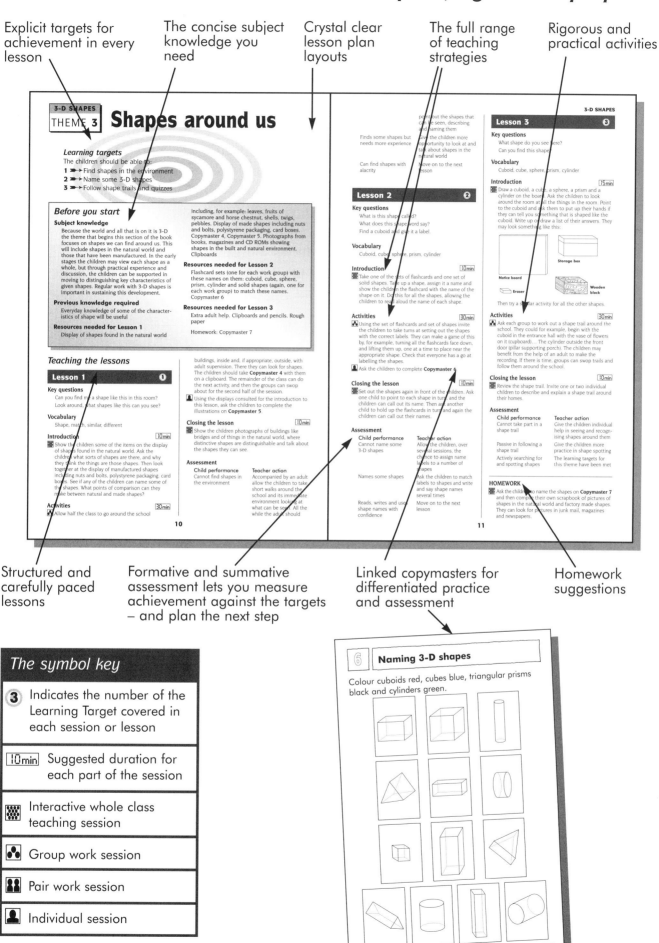

Structured and carefully paced lessons

Formative and summative assessment lets you measure achievement against the targets – and plan the next step

Linked copymasters for differentiated practice and assessment

Homework suggestions

The symbol key

3	Indicates the number of the Learning Target covered in each session or lesson
10min	Suggested duration for each part of the session
▓	Interactive whole class teaching session
⣿	Group work session
👥	Pair work session
👤	Individual session

INTRODUCTION

Learning Targets: *Shape, Space and Measures Key Stage* 1 includes lessons on all of the main ideas in shape, space and measures for children aged 5–7 (Years R–2/P1–3). Together with its companion book *Learning Targets*: *Number Key Stage* 1, it offers support for the teaching of all the key features of mathematics suitable for children of this age group. In planning and writing this book the authors have not only sought to meet the requirements of the National Curriculum (England and Wales), and Curriculum and Assessment in Scotland: National Guidelines: Mathematics 5–14, but have also borne in mind the fact that there are currently demands for teachers to use direct and whole class teaching as a regular part of their teaching repertoire, and that teachers need to be aware of and address the imperatives highlighted in the National Numeracy Project.

This book and its companion volume do not, of course, constitute a complete scheme. They cannot provide you with all the resources needed for every mathematics session. As they cover all of the main ideas in mathematics work, however, these books are a backbone resource for mathematics teaching. There are some lessons at each level of work appropriate for the Key Stages. These texts can, therefore, be seen as an extremely valuable and effective aid to the delivery of directly taught lessons. They contain a series of well-structured, detailed and specific lesson plans, backed by linked Copymasters, which you can use to teach lessons in line with national curricula and the National Numeracy Project.

As each of the four mathematics books in the series addresses work at a whole Key Stage (either Years R–2/P1–3 or Years 3–6/P4–7), it is necessary to select lessons at the appropriate level. To help you do this, the books are organised into sections which each contain a number of themes. There is a progression from the start of each section to its end. Within each theme there are three lessons which also offer a progression, and the lessons should, therefore, be taught in order.

How this book is organised

Sections

This book is organised into five sections: Introducing Shape; 3-D Shapes; 2-D Shapes; Position and Movement; and Measures and Data.

At the start of each section you will find a short overview of the mathematics ideas which we see as important in offering the children appropriate learning opportunities. A section is divided into a number of themes, each with its own set of clear learning targets. There is a progression within each section. To conclude each section there is a set of extension ideas. These can be used in any mathematics session where the key ideas related to this section are being worked on. They may be incorporated within a programme of lessons, used in sessions that immediately follow learning target lessons, used in sessions designated as mathematical investigation sessions or used as additional homework activities.

Themes

The order of the themes within each section has been arranged to offer progression. Thus, in the second section, 3-D Shapes, there are five themes. The first theme, 'Shapes around us', may be seen as more appropriate for children at an earlier stage in their mathematical education than the next theme, 'Cubes and cuboids'. Thus, 'Shapes around us' might be the theme tackled in Year R/P1, while the theme on cubes and cuboids may form part of the course for a Year 1/P2 class of children. The themes that follow place an increasing demand on children's mathematical skills and knowledge, and might therefore be taught to children in the latter part of Year 1/P2 or in Year 2/P3.

Within each theme, the lessons are also sequenced to provide more demand as the children move on from the first, to second and then third. The learning targets state explicitly what the children should know or be able to do by the end of each lesson. The learning targets provide you with a clear set of assessable objectives.

The themes in a section altogether form an overall set of lesson plans for a mathematics topic. The themes are free-standing. It is also possible for you to choose lessons from within a theme as free-standing lessons. At the end of each lesson there are descriptions of children's performance and suggested teacher actions. At the end of each theme there are suggestions for homework activities.

The lesson plans with each theme are very specific and detailed in their teaching suggestions, written to allow you to undertake direct teaching to clear objectives. Some lessons have accompanying Copymasters which are completely integrated into the teaching activities.

National curricula and numeracy

The lessons in this book have been written to meet the time demands of the 'numeracy hour' and the mathematical ideas match the required range of work in national curricula and those seen as important in the National Numeracy Project.

The need to revisit mathematics topics as children progress through Key Stage 1 (Year R–2/P1–3) has meant that the book is organised into sections which, as already indicated, can be used flexibly across the whole age range. The lessons are written so that the teacher can differentiate between children's learning by the outcomes of their work.

Each theme can provide the material for a string of numeracy hours. Every teacher will interpret the demands of the numeracy hour in the light of their own situation and the structure of the book allows for this. To plan your number work it is suggested that you consult the appropriate section and theme title to locate the lesson you want when you wish to offer a direct teaching session to your class.

The learning targets for each theme have been mapped against the Programme of Study in the National Curriculum for England and Wales, Levels 1–3 and areas in the National Numeracy Project Recommendations. These charts are presented on pages viii–ix.

The learning targets for each theme have also been mapped against the statements in the attainment targets in Curriculum and Assessment in Scotland: National Guidelines: Mathematics 5–14 at Levels A and B. This chart is presented on page x. Teachers in Scotland can therefore be confident that the lessons in this book meet the requirements to which they are working.

Curriculum planners
National Numeracy Project Recommendations

Theme No.	Problems involving measures	Data handling	Vocabulary	3-D shape	2-D shape	Line symmetry	Position and direction	Movement, angle
1			●	●	●			
2			●	●	●			
3			●	●	●			
4			●	●				
5			●	●				
6			●	●				
7			●	●				
8			●		●			
9			●		●			
10			●		●			
11			●		●			
12			●		●			
13						●		
14							●	
15							●	
16								●
17							●	●
18	●							
19	●							
20	●							
21	●							
22	●							
23	●							
24	●							
25	●							
26		●						

Shape, Space and Measures

Theme No.	2a	2b	2c	3a	3b	4a	4b
1	●	●					
2	●						
3	●						
4	●	●					
5	●	●					
6	●	●					
7	●	●	●				
8	●	●					
9	●						
10	●	●					
11	●	●					
12	●	●					
13	●	●	●				
14				●			
15	●			●			
16							●
17	●						●
18						●	
19						●	
20						●	
21						●	
22					●	●	
23					●	●	
24					●	●	
25					●	●	
26							

Curriculum planners
Scottish guidelines planner

LEVEL A	LEVEL B
INFORMATION HANDLING ATTAINMENT TARGET	
Collect	

Obtain information from a picture, video, or story
   Theme 26
Collect information about selves
	Obtain information from pictures, diagrams
	   Theme 26
	Conduct a class survey

Organise	
Tallying Theme 26 Counting Sorting into specific sets	Use a tally sheet Use a simple database
Display	

Using real objects
 	
Using pictures
   Theme 26
Drawing simple diagrams
   Theme 26
	Using labels, charts or diagrams
	   Theme 26
	Constructing a bar graph, graduated in units

Interpret	
From displays, locating and counting	From displays asking specific questions
NUMBER, MONEY AND MEASUREMENT* ATTAINMENT TARGET	
Measure and estimate	

Non-standard units: length etc.
   Themes 18, 19, 20
Place pairs of objects in order
   Themes 18, 19
Estimate length
   Theme 22
Use and understand vocabulary
   Themes 18, 19, 20, 22
	Length
	   Theme 22
	Weight
	   Themes 19, 23
	Order objects in length and weight
	   Themes 18, 19, 23
	Use abbreviations
	   Themes 22, 23
	Length conservation
	Read scales
	   Theme 22

Time	

Events in time sequence
   Theme 21
Time activities in non-standard units
   Theme 21
Tell the time in whole hours
   Theme 25
	Events in time sequence
	   Theme 21
	Tell time using analogue displays
	   Theme 25
	Read time using digital displays
	   Theme 25

SHAPE, POSITION AND MOVEMENT ATTAINMENT TARGET	
Range of shapes	

Classify shapes
   Themes 1, 2, 8
Identify and name cubes, cones, cylinders ans spheres
   Themes 3, 4, 5
Identify and name squares, triangles and circles
   Themes 8, 9, 11
Create and copy 3D structures
   Theme 7
	Respond to written/oral descriptions of shapes
	   Themes 7, 8, 9
	Identify and name triangular/square pyramid
	   Theme 6
	Find shapes that will tile
	   Themes 7, 12
	Make 3D shapes
	   Themes 5, 6, 7

Position and movement	

Position and movement of object
   Themes 4, 15
Locate an object in the classroom
   Themes 4, 15
	Give and understand instructions for turning through right angles
	   Themes 16, 17
	Recognise and name the four compass points
	
	Use grid references
	Create a square or rectangle
	   Theme 9

Symmetry	
	Recognise symmetrical shapes Themes 12, 13
Angles	
	Draw right angle Theme 16

*For coverage of number and money see the companion book: *Learning Targets: Number Key Stage 1*.

INTRODUCING SHAPE

Children learn about the world around them by exploring patterns and the relationships between objects. They define cats and dogs on the basis of their characteristics, while recognising some variations in size, colour and hair length. This ability to identify things and name them applies not only to the animate. Exploring pattern in shapes is also something of which young children are capable. When exploring shapes the youngster is also interested in the position of objects in relation to each other. This is why spaces are interesting too. Space only has meaning when there are objects within the space. Then we can look at position, movement and the distances between objects and their magnitude. This is why, in mathematics, we relate shape, space and measures.

In Introducing Shape we are concerned with the foundations of later work on two and three dimensions, and all of the measures of objects in space. The first steps are about similarities and differences and the language that allows us to describe perceived relationships and distinctions. The importance of the acquisition of vocabulary to describe shape, position, movement and dimensions cannot be over-emphasised. Without such a vocabulary the child will not be able to progress in their ability to communicate their ideas and

understandings about shape, space and measures. This ability is not merely for the purposes of fulfilling school work demands but is an important part of the way in which as adults, we need to be able to relate to our built environment and the artefacts that we use in our everyday lives.

To the faculties of sight and language we need to add touch. There is much that we all learn through handling objects; not only texture but also shape. We often describe three-dimensional objects using aspects of their features such as two-dimensional shapes and relative sizes. Within size we would include mass and volume as well as the more obvious measures of length. This means that not only should the children learn the names of common shapes and be able to describe their features, but also that they should have lots of opportunity for practical work. In using tactile, auditory and oral exploration of shapes and spaces there are three considerations that we need to keep in mind. These are the need for confirmation in repeated experiences with familiar shapes; construction in the exploration of objects in terms of their physical characteristics and how they might fit together; and comparison in looking at the similarities and differences between shapes, spaces and objects.

THEME 1

Vocabulary of shape

Learning targets

The children should be able to:

1 ➤➤ Explore and model with shapes
2 ➤➤ Begin to use mathematical words to describe shapes
3 ➤➤ Read and write words about shapes

Before you start

Subject knowledge

At the beginning of their work on shape, children will have a vast experience of what shapes look like, what their features are, what we use them for and where they are found. They may not be able to articulate this experience and also may know none of the shape vocabulary, that is the mathematical jargon, that they need to master to handle shape work in the future. In this theme there are lessons showing that we can begin with everyday words the children use, and then introduce them to mathematical terms. Note that the intention here is that the children should be consolidating their describing words for shape, both those they use themselves and those that are used by the teacher. Shape names will come in subsequent themes. If some children can name shapes this is fine, but knowing and naming can be different and so we are working on an understanding of shape features.

Previous knowledge required

'Everyday life' experience of shapes

Resources needed for Lesson 1

Construction sets that have blocks of different shapes in them. Some pieces of card cut into irregular shapes. Extra adult help would be invaluable in model-making. Junk packaging, strong sticky tape (or PVA glue), kitchen cloths, empty food trays, poster paint made up to thick consistency, overalls and newspaper to protect the children and the tables

Resources needed for Lesson 2

Simple display of shaped objects. Collection of objects the children can handle. It would be useful to have a matching collection for each work group in the class (each object colour coded) such as a matchbox, poster tube, four-sided piece of card (not regular), popcorn cup, giant dice, skipping rope, large pencil, pizza box, pointed party hat, heart-shaped piece of card; or a similar set of items (see closing the lesson), and a 'feely' bag (a clean and empty cloth PE pump bag is ideal) to put them in.

Resources needed for Lesson 3

Book of blank sugar paper pages made up before the lesson. Blank flashcards and a large felt-tipped pen. Copymaster 1. Some solid and flat shapes for use at the end of the lesson.

Teaching the lessons

Lesson 1   ①

Key questions

Tell me about this shape.

What can you say about this shape?

Talk about the shape of your favourite toy.

How many shapes have you used in your model? Tell me about them.

Vocabulary

Shape, flat, thickness (and words the children use which may include, for example, oblong, sharp, round, pointy, curvy)

Introduction   5 min

Tell the children that they are going to be working on shapes. Show them a solid shape and a flat shape cut from card. Talk about these shapes, showing that the one is flat and the other is not. Invite children to come and hold up a flat shape, or one that is not, or match a 'not flat' shape with another that is 'not flat'.

Activities   40 min

Give the children the opportunity to make a model from junk packaging. If there is extra adult help available, adults can help the children to bind their boxes together using strong sticky tape. If not they will need to use PVA glue and leave the model until the glue hardens. While a group of children do this activity, other groups can do the other activities and then the children can swop around.

Using boxes, corks, bottle tops and pieces of card and empty packaging, the children can make some prints of shapes. Printing pads should be made by placing pieces of kitchen cloth in empty food trays and then pouring poster paint over them. The resulting outlines of flat shapes can be discussed with the children and be set on display.

Invite the children to use the construction toys to make towers, buildings and other models. Ask them which sorts of shape are best to build with, which shapes they find hard to use, and which shapes are good for special jobs.

Closing the lesson | 10 min |

This lesson yields a vast quantity of children's work. Choose one or two junk models, print pictures and construction models for the whole class to look at and comment on. The work can be set up as part of a display which will be added to in the next lesson.

Assessment

Child performance	Teacher action
Makes no contribution to shape discussion and exploration	Individually or in a small group, allow the children time to explore shapes and talk about what he or she is doing
Explores and models with shapes	Allow the child more opportunities to talk about the work done
Explores, models and has an understanding of some shape features	Move on to the next lesson

Lesson 2 ②

Key questions

What words describe this shape?

Tell me about the shape in the feely bag.

Vocabulary

Corner, edge, face (of a shape) (and words the children use, including, for example, sharp, curved, pointed, smooth, roll)

Introduction | 10 min |

Show the children things that have been set out on the display. Talk about the first shape picked up. For example, if this is a wooden box, describe it by saying things like: it is long, has thickness, has corners, has eight corners, has flat sides, and has a lid which is the same shape but a bit narrower than the box. Then pick up another shape and ask one of the children to describe it. Do the same with other shapes on display.

Activities | 30 min |

Give the children a collection of objects they can handle. It would be useful to have a matching set for each work group in the class. Set out the group of objects in front of each of the groups in the class. They should be painted or colour coded so that the

children can pick up each in turn. Ask the groups to allow one of the children to pick up the red object. Now go around the class asking the child holding the object in each group to say something about it (each child should say something different). Then go around each group again, asking the whole group to say something else about the shape. Finally throw the discussion open so that other words and phrases are added. Then ask another child to pick up the green object. Repeat this process until all shapes are described and all children have had a go.

Take a shape from a construction set, without the children seeing, and place it in a feely bag. Ask a child to come out to the front, and, while feeling the object in the bag, describe it. They can then pull the shape out of the bag and hold it up. Repeat this for more shapes, with a different child each time.

Closing the lesson | 10 min |

Give each group two shapes which they have not worked with before (preferably two shapes which they have not seen) making sure the shapes for each group are different. For example, here is a list which would fit a class with five work groups:

matchbox	poster tube
four-sided piece of card (not regular)	heart-shaped piece of card
giant dice	skipping rope
large pencil	pizza box
pointed party hat	popcorn cup

Ask the groups to see how many words they can use to describe each shape. Choose two groups to share their words with the rest of the class.

Assessment

Child performance	Teacher action
Talks about shapes	Individually or in a small group, talk with the children about shapes, injecting some mathematical words into the discussion
Begins to use mathematical words to describe shapes	Go on to the next lesson
Has mastered some of the vocabulary of shape and uses it with confidence	Go on to the next lesson, allowing the children to initiate the learning of others

Lesson 3 ③

Key questions

What does this word say?

Can you write 'corner', 'face',...?

Vocabulary

As well as the children's own words, they will need to be using the following: corner, face, edge, flat, curved

INTRODUCING SHAPE

Introduction | 15min

Note that this lesson is about words describing shapes, and not their names, which will appear in specific themes. Remind the children of their work in the previous lesson. Show the children the large book of blank sugar paper pages and ask them to help compile a list of words about shapes for the class book. Write the words the children give you on the board or on blank flashcards with a large felt-tipped pen. The set of words can then be held up, one at a time and the children can read each aloud. These words can be stuck into the book later in the day.

Activities | 30min

 Give each child **Copymaster 1** and ask them to copy out the shape words. They can then cut them out as flashcards ready for the next activity.

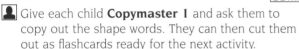 Ask the children to play at matching and reading out the pairs of words in their own set. Walk around and check that the children are reading the words correctly as they play. They can also place their words face down and mix them up with those of their partner. They can then take turns at turning up two words and try to find matching pairs. At the end of the game the players can discard all the hand written words and take one set of printed words away for their own word box or book.

Closing the lesson | 5min

 Using some of the words the children have given at the beginning of the lesson, or the flashcard words from Copymaster 1, allow a child to set these labels alongside appropriate shapes while the rest of the class look on.

Assessment

Child performance	Teacher action
Cannot read and write words about shapes	Beginning with the children's own words help them compile a shape word book, and check their learning with a shape task or talk each day.
Reads and writes shape words but needs more practice.	Give the children more practice
Reads and writes shape words with confidence.	The learning targets for this theme have been met.

HOMEWORK

Ask the children to make a shape model from packaging at home. They can write out some of the shape words they have learned and stick them on their model in the appropriate places. These could be brought to school and set up as a display for the children to look at, as shown below.

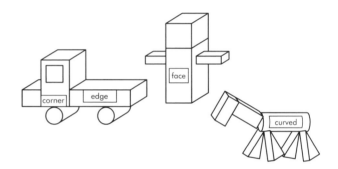

Matching and ordering

Learning targets

The children should be able to:

1 ➡➤ Match shapes
2 ➡➤ Sort shapes
3 ➡➤ Place shapes in order

Before you start

Subject knowledge

This theme is an introduction to some of the spatial aspects of shape: concepts like size, matching, orientation and order. If the children have already had copious experience of shape work, they will already be using some shape names and can be given more as they come to need them. It is important though, that the children do not apply labels until they demonstrate a knowledge (whether they articulate it or not) of the features of shapes to which they are wanting to give a name.

Previous knowledge required

'Everyday life' experience of shapes, an understanding of concepts like size and order.

Resources needed for Lesson 1

Vast collection of three dimensional shapes, and a collection of flat shapes cut from card. These should include regular and irregular shapes. Copymaster 2

Resources needed for Lesson 2

A box of shapes for each work group. The boxes can contain a mix of any of the following: cube, cuboid, sphere, cylinder, prism, pyramid, square, rectangle, triangle, circle, pentagon, hexagon. The shapes do not need to all be regular. In fact some irregular shapes should be included. Copymaster 3

Resources needed for Lesson 3

Set of three cuboids (empty food packs are fine) each covered in a different colour of paper. Sticky paper shapes, and paper on which to stick them. Templates of two dimensional shapes of a range of different sizes. Collection of three dimensional shapes including at least three each of the following: cuboid, sphere, cube, triangular or hexagonal prism

Homework: book of blank sugar paper pages made up before the lesson (see page 7)

Teaching the lessons

Lesson 1   ❶

Key questions

Can you find a shape like this?

Which shape matches this one?

Vocabulary

Match, same (words and shape names the children use)

Introduction   `10min`

Allow individual children to come to the front of the class where there is a collection of shapes set out. Pick up a shape and ask the child to find one to match it. Ask them how they know it matches. Give the child several goes. Then invite another child to do this task. The class can look on.

Activities   `30min`

A group at a time can do this activity while the remainder of the class get on with the other activities. Give the children a selection of shapes and ask them to take turns at sorting them and putting those that they think similar together. Ask the children about their sorts, and ask other children in the group if they can explain what features the child has used to create the sort.

Ask the children to complete **Copymaster 2** where they can match shapes together.

Closing the lesson   `10min`

Set out about 6 different shapes around the room, and in different locations include another 6 that are the same shape (but not identical). Number the shapes 1 to 12. Ask the children to write the number of a shape on a piece of paper and then next to it the number of the matching shape. They can complete this for all six shapes.

In a whole class group, check and talk about the 'matches' that the children have made.

Assessment

Child performance	Teacher action
Cannot match shapes	Give the children 'play' experience with model making and mosaics so that they handle both three and two dimensional shapes.
Matches shapes but lacks confidence	Give more opportunities to handle shapes and set them alongside one another to make comparisons and matches
Adept at matching shapes	Move on to the next lesson

Lesson 2 ②

Key questions

Can you tell me about the way you have sorted these?

Why have you put all these together?

Can you see how I have sorted these?

Vocabulary

Side, face, surface, (and shape names and other vocabulary used by the children)

Introduction ⬚5min

▦ Show the children one of the boxes of shapes prepared for the activity in the lesson. Take all the shapes out, and place them in two sets (flat shapes and not flat shapes). Show the children that you have sorted them out, and ask how the sort has been made. Tell them that they will now have turns at sorting.

Activities ⬚35min

⚫⚫ Give the children time with their box of shapes so that each child has a turn at sorting out the shapes, while the rest of the group look on. Ask the children if each of them can find a different way of sorting. Visit each group to see how the children are getting on.

👤 Ask each child to complete **Copymaster 3** where they can place shapes in sets.

Closing the lesson ⬚10min

▦ Ask each group to show one of the sorts they made with their shapes. Ask the child who did the sort to stay at the table and explain their sort, while all the other children visit all the tables and inspect the sorts made.

Assessment

Child performance	Teacher action
Cannot sort shapes	Allow children to handle shapes while describing them to the teacher. Encourage them to point out the similarities and
	differences between shapes
Sorts shapes, but cannot use a range of features	Give more practice in sorting
Sorts shapes readily	Move on to next lesson

Lesson 3 ③

Key questions

Can you put these in order of size?

Can you continue the pattern? What comes next?

Vocabulary

Small, smaller, smallest, large, larger, largest, next, before, after, order

Introduction ⬚5min

▦ Using the set of three cuboids of different sizes and colours, set them out in a row in front of the children. Begin with the smallest, then the next in size, and then the next. Point out to the children that you have placed them in order. Ask them how you have ordered them. Take the boxes away and place them in order again, this time starting with the largest. Ask the children to remember that the way they order the shapes in their work is important in this lesson.

Activities ⬚35min

▦ 👤 Allow each child to make a pattern using sticky shapes. Remind them that the pattern should have an order. Before they begin, draw the following pattern on the board:

Ask the children what comes next, and what comes after that. Emphasise that their pattern should show a 'repeat' in the order of shapes they have chosen.

👥 Ask the children to create rows of their shapes in size order by drawing around the templates.

Closing the lesson ⬚10min

▦ Using the three dimensional shape collection, set out, for example, one cuboid, one sphere and one triangular prism in a row in front of the children. Ask a child to come and continue the pattern by putting the next shape in the row, repeat this again and again until all the children can see the order of the shapes. Remove the shapes and begin another pattern for the children to continue.

Assessment

Child performance
Cannot place shapes in order

Orders shapes but lacks confidence

Teacher action
Give the children individual help in pattern replication and prediction, before giving more opportunities at pattern creation

Give more practice at pattern replication and creation

Confidently creates and replicates order patterns

The learning targets for this theme have been met

HOMEWORK

Give the children a small book made up from sugar paper pages which they can take home. Ask them to make a 'What comes next?' book with patterns of their own such as shown below.

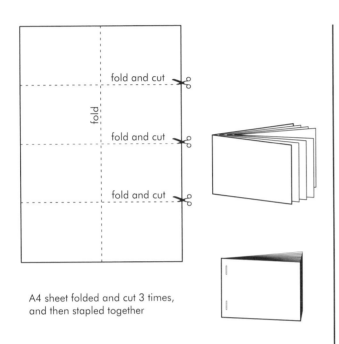

A4 sheet folded and cut 3 times, and then stapled together

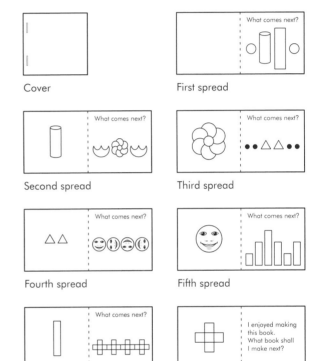

Cover

First spread

Second spread

Third spread

Fourth spread

Fifth spread

Sixth spread

Seventh spread

Investigations

- Give lots of opportunities for sand and water play using different shapes and containers.
- Make a collection of objects and get groups of children to sort them and then display their sorts for the rest of the class. Each group could have a week for their sorts to be on display.
- Put different shapes in a cloth bag and get the children to feel the shape and give verbal clues so that others can attempt to name the shape.
- Make or purchase sets of dominoes that have shapes on them. The children have to match the shapes. 'Snap' can also be played using cards with shapes on them.
- Using geoboards with nine pins, elastic bands and large squared paper the children can make shapes and record examples of those they create.
- Use gummed shapes and/ or flannelgraph to allow the children to make pictures and patterns using 2-D shapes.
- With the children taking turns to act as the 'director', take photographs in and around the school, of features that the children see as having interesting shapes or dimensions. Put these on display and get different children to talk about what they find interesting about the pictures and the real objects.

Assessment

- Using commercially produced attribute material the children should work together to sort in ways that they define. They should be able to articulate the reasons for their sorts.
- Give the children a sheet of line drawings of regular and irregular 2-D shapes. Ask the children to link the shapes that 'match' or go together.
- Get the children to sort given shapes on the basis of sides, then corners; then sides and corners.

3-D SHAPES

Ours is a three-dimensional world. All the shapes in it are 3-D. We, and the objects around us, have length, width and depth. Even sheets of card or paper, ink and fabrics have thickness; though for everyday purposes we think of them as 2-D. It is therefore a fundamental part of the child's understanding of the world, that they know some of the features of different 3-D shapes, and where they may be found. Again we need to draw attention to the importance of language – some might use length, height and width, for example. Also it is important to understand that though, logically, we ought to start with a study of three-dimensional shapes then move to two dimensions it is the case that, in school, we commonly do it the other way round. It is also the case that in trying to describe and discuss three-dimensional objects we often use their faces and describe them using two-dimensional vocabulary. So three- and two-dimensional work should necessarily be linked.

In the early stages it is important to give the children lots of practical work with three-dimensional shapes. In describing the characteristics of such shapes the discussion should not be confined to sides, edges and corners but should also embrace features such as rolling or sliding. There should also be a continuing opportunity for the children to build with three-dimensional shapes. Many will have had pre-school experiences of such building though some may not. Both materials that are designed for construction and everyday objects, which can be utilised in constructional play, should be employed. Making suggestions such as building a model of a farm or castle can follow free play in construction.

After the children have had lots of experiences of sorting three-dimensional shapes and building with them they ought to be in a position to start to formally organise their evaluations of the characteristics of 3-D shapes. In these evaluations we are looking for discussion about sides or edges in number and shape; faces in number and shape, stability, does it roll or topple depending on how it is placed; overall features including size, similarities and differences with other 3D shapes. As the children move into offering descriptions of the 3-D shapes we commonly use in classrooms it will happen that they start to describe some using 2-D vocabulary. For example, it is quite common for children to talk about a cube as being 'square'. We have to be sensitive to what is meant by this kind of assertion and not inhibit the children by too quickly pointing out that this is a description of one face not of the whole object.

THEME 3 Shapes around us

Learning targets

The children should be able to:

1 ➡➤ Find shapes in the environment

2 ➡➤ Name some 3-D shapes

3 ➡➤ Follow shape trails and quizzes

Before you start

Subject knowledge

Because the world and all that is on it is 3-D the theme that begins this section of the book focuses on shapes we can find around us. This will include shapes in the natural world and those that have been manufactured. In the early stages the children may view each shape as a whole, but through practical experience and discussion, the children can be supported in moving to distinguishing key characteristics of given shapes. Regular work with 3-D shapes is important in sustaining this development.

Previous knowledge required

Everyday knowledge of some of the characteristics of shape will be useful

Resources needed for Lesson 1

Display of shapes found in the natural world including, for example: leaves, fruits of sycamore and horse chestnut, shells, twigs, pebbles. Display of made shapes including nuts and bolts, polystyrene packaging, card boxes. Copymaster 4, Copymaster 5. Photographs from books, magazines and CD ROMs showing shapes in the built and natural environment. Clipboards

Resources needed for Lesson 2

Flashcard sets (one for each work group) with these names on them: cuboid, cube, sphere, prism, cylinder and solid shapes (again, one for each work group) to match these names. Copymaster 6

Resources needed for Lesson 3

Extra adult help. Clipboards and pencils. Rough paper

Homework: Copymaster 7

Teaching the lessons

Lesson 1 ①

Key questions

Can you find me a shape like this in this room?

Look around, what shapes like this can you see?

Vocabulary

Shape, match, similar, different

Introduction | 10 min |

▓ Show the children some of the items on the display of shapes found in the natural world. Ask the children what sorts of shapes are there, and why they think the things are those shapes. Then look together at the display of manufactured shapes including nuts and bolts, polystyrene packaging. card boxes. See if any of the children can name some of the shapes. What points of comparison can they make between natural and made shapes?

Activities | 30 min |

 Allow half the class to go around the school buildings, inside and, if appropriate, outside, with adult supervision. There they can look for shapes. The children should take **Copymaster 4** with them on a clipboard. The remainder of the class can do the next activity, and then the groups can swop about for the second half of the session.

👤 Using the displays consulted for the introduction to this lesson, ask the children to complete the illustrations on **Copymaster 5**.

Closing the lesson | 10 min |

▓ Show the children photographs of buildings like bridges and of things in the natural world, where distinctive shapes are distinguishable and talk about the shapes they can see.

Assessment

Child performance	Teacher action
Cannot find shapes in the environment	Accompanied by an adult allow the children to take short walks around the school and its immediate environment looking at what can be seen. All the while the adult should

point out the shapes that can be seen, describing and naming them

| Finds some shapes but needs more experience | Give the children more opportunity to look at and talk about shapes in the natural world |
| Can find shapes with alacrity | Move on to the next lesson |

Lesson 2 ②

Key questions

What is this shape called?

What does this shape word say?

Find a cuboid and give it a label.

Vocabulary

Cuboid, cube, sphere, prism, cylinder

Introduction 10 min

 Take one of the sets of flashcards and one set of solid shapes. Take up a shape, assign it a name and show the children the flashcard with the name of the shape on it. Do this for all the shapes, allowing the children to read aloud the name of each shape.

Activities 30 min

 Using the set of flashcards and set of shapes invite the children to take turns at setting out the shapes with the correct labels. They can make a game of this by, for example, turning all the flashcards face down, and lifting them up, one at a time to place near the appropriate shape. Check that everyone has a go at labelling the shapes.

Ask the children to complete **Copymaster 6**.

Closing the lesson 10 min

 Set out the shapes again in front of the children. Ask one child to point to each shape in turn, and the children can call out its name. Then ask another child to hold up the flashcards in turn and again the children can call out their names.

Assessment

Child performance	Teacher action
Cannot name some 3-D shapes	Allow the children, over several sessions, the chance to assign name labels to a number of shapes
Names some shapes	Ask the children to match labels to shapes and write and say shape names several times
Reads, writes and uses shape names with confidence	Move on to the next lesson

Lesson 3 ③

Key questions

What shape do you see here?

Can you find this shape?

Vocabulary

Cuboid, cube, sphere, prism, cylinder

Introduction 15 min

 Draw a cuboid, a cube, a sphere, a prism and a cylinder on the board. Ask the children to look around the room at all the things in the room. Point to the cuboid and ask them to put up their hands if they can tell you something that is shaped like the cuboid. Write up or draw a list of their answers. They may look something like this:

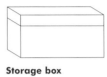

Storage box

Notice board

 Eraser

 Wooden block

Then try a similar activity for all the other shapes.

Activities 30 min

 Ask each group to work out a shape trail around the school. They could for example, begin with the cuboid in the entrance hall with the vase of flowers on it (cupboard)… The cylinder outside the front door (pillar supporting porch). The children may benefit from the help of an adult to make the recording. If there is time, groups can swop trails and follow them around the school.

Closing the lesson 10 min

 Review the shape trail. Invite one or two individual children to describe and explain a shape trail around their homes.

Assessment

Child performance	Teacher action
Cannot take part in a shape trail	Give the children individual help in seeing and recognising shapes around them
Passive in following a shape trail	Give the children more practice in shape spotting
Actively searching for and spotting shapes	The learning targets for this theme have been met

HOMEWORK

 Ask the children to name the shapes on **Copymaster 7** and then compile their own scrapbook of pictures of shapes in the natural world and factory made shapes. They can look for pictures in junk mail, magazines and newspapers.

Cubes and cuboids

Learning targets

The children should be able to:

1 ➡➤ Sort and match cubes and cuboids and describe them
2 ➡➤ Compare and contrast the features of different cuboids
3 ➡➤ Know what a cube and cuboid look like when opened out

Before you start

Subject knowledge

This theme is intended to give children sufficient experience to have a good understanding of what a cuboid is, and what a cube (which is a special case of a cuboid) is. Cuboids are very important in terms of human experience. They are to be found in the built environment and are commonly used in packaging.

Previous knowledge required

A good vocabulary of words to talk about shapes

Resources needed for Lesson 1

Collections of at least 10 cubes and cuboids for each work group in the class, Copymasters 8 and 9

Resources needed for Lesson 2

A grocery, shoe or other large cardboard box. Cuboid cartons (enough for one for each pair of children). Rough paper. Copymaster 9

Resources needed for Lesson 3

Cartons and food packaging (cuboid) that can be opened out. One cube box that can be cut open; scissors. Large sheets of sugar paper. Copymasters 10 and 11

Teaching the lessons

Lesson 1 ①

Key questions

Can you find me a cuboid here?
What is this shape called?
You say this is not a cube. How do you know that?

Vocabulary

Cuboid, cube, face, edge, corner

Introduction ⏲ 10min

▦ Show the children a cuboid box, and a cuboid box that has been cut into pieces as shown here.

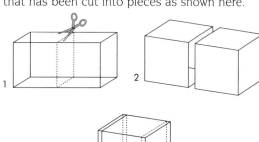

3
Push one cut edge
into the other until
exact cube is made

Remind the children the shape is called a cuboid. Write the word cuboid on the board. Then show the children that if we make a cuboid with all edges the same, the shape we make is called a cube. Write the word 'cube' on the board.

Activities ⏲ 30min

♣ Ask the children to talk together about their collections of cubes and cuboids. They can take turns at naming the shapes, sorting them into cubes and cuboids, placing them in size order, naming things they know that are these shapes and sizes.

▤ Ask each child to complete **Copymaster 8**.

▥▥ Ask the children to make a list or draw all the things they can think of that are cube- or cuboid-shaped.

Closing the lesson ⏲ 10min

▦ Assemble all the ideas the children have about where we find cubes and cuboids. Here are some to add to the children's suggestions: cube – ice, sugar, dice, cuboid – video recorder, flat roofed building, cereal box, computer disk box.

Assessment

Child performance	Teacher action
Cannot sort and match cubes and cuboids	Give the children short practical sessions and opportunities to handle, play with and model with shapes. Talk about their

Can sort and match cubes and cuboids and describe them

work, giving them the chance to use shape names and talk about shapes

Move on to the next lesson

Can determine the features of cubes and cuboids and articulate them while sorting

Move on to the next lesson, noting that the children will need extension challenges

identifying and comparing features

Can discuss cuboid features

Move on to the next lesson

Lesson 2

Key questions

Can you find a shape like this?

How does this cuboid differ from this one?

Vocabulary

Cuboid, cube, face, edge, corner

Introduction 15min

Hold up the large cuboid box and point to a face, an edge and a corner. Write these words on the board and invite two children, in turn, to come out and hold up a cuboid shape, pointing to and naming these features. Then hold up two boxes, including, for example, a toothpaste box and a cereal pack. Ask a child to come and describe how these differ from one another. Check that the child talks about the lengths of the sides. Ask another child to choose two different cuboid boxes and discuss those in a similar way.

Activities 30min

Ask the children to investigate a cuboid, and on rough paper make a record of how many of the following all cuboids have: faces, edges and corners.

Hold up the large box again and ask the children how many faces it has. Check out the number 6 by counting the faces in front of the children. Then ask how many edges there are, and count the 12. Finally count the eight corners of the cuboid.

Ask the children to complete **Copymaster 9**.

Closing the lesson 5min

Ask the children some quick-fire questions about cuboids. Here are some example questions:

- Are they good for building? Why?
- Can they be all sizes from very small to very big?
- What is the smallest cuboid you can think of and the largest?
- What would not be the same in a kitchen if we had no cuboids?

Assessment

Child performance	Teacher action
Cannot compare and contrast the features of different cuboids	Give the children individual support in handling and talking about shapes
Points out the features of cuboids but lacks confidence	Allow the children to handle cuboids and have more practice in

Lesson 3

Key questions

Can you match this shape to its net?

What is this the net of?

Vocabulary

Net, cuboid, cube, face, edge, corner

Introduction 15min

Take a cuboid box, preferably a large one like a cereal box, and cut or prise it open carefully in front of the children. Fold the cut shape up to make the box again, and then open it out and spread it out so that the children can see the shape. Draw around the outline of the shape on the board and mark in the fold lines so that the children can see them. Then take a box that is cube shaped and do the same activity.

Activities 30min

Allow the children to open out a carton, just as you did in the introduction. Each of the two children can then draw around it to make their own net of a cuboid

Ask the children to complete **Copymaster 10** where they are matching shapes to nets.

Closing the lesson 10min

Using the shape and net cards made up from **Copymaster 11** (which can, if you wish, be enlarged on a suitable photocopier) ask a child to hold up a shape so that the rest of the class can see it, and another child can find and hold up the appropriate net card. Try this for all the set of shapes and nets.

Assessment

Child performance	Teacher action
Gives no sign of knowing what a cube and cuboid look like when opened out	Allow the children to open out a series of cuboid boxes and discuss what they see
Knows what a net is but finds it difficult to match shapes to their nets	Give the children more practice at matching and looking at shapes when folded and when opened out
Knows about the nets of a cuboid and a cube	The learning targets for this theme have been met

HOMEWORK

Invite the children to make models using cuboid packaging. Good topics might include robots, houses, trucks, lorries and Scottie dogs. The models would make a contribution to a shape display.

Cylinders, cones and spheres

Learning targets

The children should be able to:

1 ➤➤ Identify cylinders, and describe them

2 ➤➤ Identify spheres and cones and describe them

3 ➤➤ Make a shape book and explore what happens when we slice through a cylinder, a sphere and a cone

Before you start

Subject knowledge

In this theme the children should be taught to recognise and name cylinders and the less common shapes, spheres and cones. During the lessons the children should gain experiences that enable them to name some of the features of these shapes. Whilst cylinders are quite easy to recognise they are not so easy to describe. Strictly, a cylinder is a prism which has two faces at the ends which are congruent circles, and also a curved surface. There are no vertices.

Previous knowledge required

Practical everyday experience of shapes

Resources needed for Lesson 1

A collection of 'junk' packs shaped like cylinders. Common examples include containers which held chocolate sweets, drinking chocolate, gravy granules, posters and kitchen cleaning powder. The card tubes inside paper kitchen towel and foil offer open cylinders. Include also cuboid shapes, so that the children can compare them with cylinders. Copymaster 12

Resources needed for Lesson 2

A collection of balls of different sizes, a globe of the world. A cone and paper with which to make cones. A collection of shapes, including at least two of each, such as the following

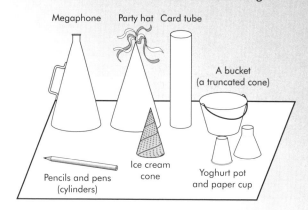

Megaphone Party hat Card tube

A bucket (a truncated cone)

Ice cream cone

Pencils and pens (cylinders)

Yoghurt pot and paper cup

Plasticine® and modelling boards, Copymaster 13. An adult helper

Resources needed for Lesson 3

Magazines, educational catalogues, plain paper and scissors, Plasticine®, a modelling board and a modelling tool (enough for each group). Made-up class 'shape' books: spherical, cylindrical and conical (see page 16)

Teaching the lessons

Lesson 1 ①

Key questions

What is this shape called?

Tell me about cylinders. What do they look like?

What do we use cylindrical shapes for? Why do we do that?

Vocabulary

Cylinder, curved, round

Introduction ⟨10min⟩

▦ Hold up several cylinders in turn and ask the children what shape they are. Tell everyone that they are called cylinders. Write the word 'cylinder' on the board. Ask the children what they know and use that comes in a cylindrical package.

Activities ⟨30min⟩

◉◉ Give each group a selection of cuboids and cylinders. Ask them to take turns at putting the cylinders together, putting the cylinders in order, and talking about where cylinders are used.

▦ While the children look on, cut open a cylindrical

box. Show the children how a cylinder looks when flattened out. The net should look something like this:

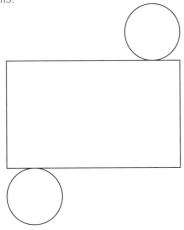

👤 Ask the children to complete **Copymaster 12**.

Closing the lesson | 10 min

▦ Set up the title 'Cylinders' on an empty display. Ask individual children to select a package or object to place on the display and say why they are putting it there. After the lesson make captions using the words and comments that the children made and place these on the display. Here is how it may look:

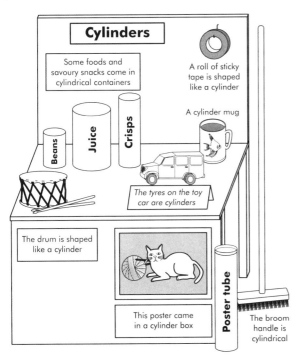

Cylinders

Some foods and savoury snacks come in cylindrical containers

A roll of sticky tape is shaped like a cylinder

A cylinder mug

Beans

Juice

Crisps

The tyres on the toy car are cylinders

The drum is shaped like a cylinder

Poster tube

This poster came in a cylinder box

The broom handle is cylindrical

Assessment

Child performance	Teacher action
Cannot identify cylinders	Give the children support in sorting shapes and talking about them. Attach name labels to cylinders and ask the children to read, say aloud and copy the names
Works with cylinders but needs more practice	Allow the children the chance to repeat activities like those in this lesson
Shows good understanding of the features of a cylinder	Move on to the next lesson

Lesson 2 ②

Key questions

What is this shape called?

Which shape here is a sphere?

Can you sort out the cones from these shapes?

Vocabulary

Sphere, cone, base, apex

Introduction | 10 min

▦ Show the children the collection of balls of different sizes. Tell the children that the shape of a perfectly round ball is called a sphere. Write the word on the board. Then show the children the cone, name it, and write its name on the board. Point to its base and its apex.

Activities | 30 min

👥 Allow a group at a time to do this activity while the other groups get on with the other activities. Give each child a fist-sized blob of Plasticine® and a board. Ask the children to make a sphere. Allow the group to use their spheres to answer these questions.

• Does a sphere roll?

• Can we stack spheres on top of one another, without the risk of them falling or changing their shape?

• Can spheres be laid together without spaces in between?

👥 Set out the collection of shapes including at least two each of the following: cones, truncated cones and cylinders. Invite the children to take turns at commenting on the similarities and differences between these shapes. They should have an adult present for this discussion.

👤 Ask the children to look for and name shapes in the picture shown on **Copymaster 13**.

Closing the lesson | 10 min

▦ Look at Copymaster 13 with the children and locate and talk about the shapes with them.

Assessment

Child performance	Teacher action
Cannot identify spheres and cones and describe them	Take opportunities every day to point out shapes and ask questions about shape, until the children show more confidence
Hesitant about describing these shapes	Allow more discussion sessions about shapes
Has a good understanding of the attributes of spheres and cones	Move on to the next lesson

Lesson 3

Key questions

What other things can we draw or cut out for the shape books?

What shape have we made here?

What shape will the cut face be if we cut here?

Vocabulary

Cylinder, sphere, cone, circle, oval, edge, apex, base, triangle

Introduction | 5 min |

Show the children the made-up class books for which they are to supply pictures. You may choose to make them like this:

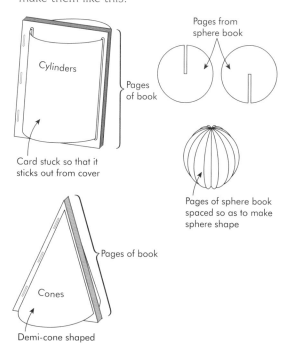

Cylinders

Card stuck so that it sticks out from cover

Pages of book

Pages from sphere book

Pages of sphere book spaced so as to make sphere shape

Pages of book

Cones

Demi-cone shaped

Cut out a picture ready to stick into the book.

Activities | 45 min |

Give each pair of children magazines, educational catalogues, plain paper and scissors. Ask them to produce three pictures for the class books. They can cut out or draw things that are spherical, cylindrical or conical.

While the children look on, take a large blob of Plasticine®, a modelling board and a tool and make the following: a sphere, a cylinder and a cone. Ask the children to predict what shape the cut face will be when you slice the sphere. Show that wherever you slice it the cut face is always circular. Then ask what will happen when you slice the cylinder. Cut it in a variety of directions and show the children the rectangular and circular cut faces. Finally cut the cone open to reveal triangular, oval (elliptical) and circular faces.

Allow the children to each take a turn at making a shape from Plasticine® and cutting through it to see the shape of the cut surfaces.

Closing the lesson | 5 min |

Hold up some of the contributions to the class shape books so that the children can see them. After the lesson, stick the pictures into the books and add them to the class library or a display.

Assessment

Child performance	Teacher action
Makes little contribution to the lesson	Give the children individual attention in handling, talking about and identifying these shapes
Reveals errors in understanding, either by what is said or what is on the Copymaster	Correct the children's errors and allow more experience of work in this area
Confident and competent with these shapes	The learning targets for this theme have been met

HOMEWORK

Invite the children to draw a little cartoon story with characters shaped like a cylinder, sphere, and cone in it. They should show in the story some of the characteristics of these shapes. They can show in pictures, or have speech bubbles or sentences written below the pictures.

Prisms and pyramids

Learning targets

The children should be able to:

1 ➤➤ Name the features of prisms and pyramids
2 ➤➤ Find prisms in the built environment
3 ➤➤ Identify the nets of prisms and pyramids

Before you start

Subject knowledge

This theme focuses on prisms and pyramids. Cuboids are in fact rectangular prisms, but are very common and assigned a special name and so have been accorded a separate theme. Triangular prisms are common as roofs. The pyramid is uncommon, both in the built environment and in packaging. However because the Pyramids of Egypt are one of the Wonders of the World, people do think of a square-based pyramid when talking about 3-D shapes.

Previous knowledge required

Awareness of 3-D shapes especially cuboids, shape description vocabulary, including, for example, face, edge, corner

Resources needed for Lesson 1

Prism-shaped boxes (enough for one for each work group), a picture of the Pyramids in Egypt, photographs of roofs, a hexagonal prism, Copymaster 14

Resources needed for Lesson 2

Access to the grounds around the school and to other buildings in the neighbourhood. Large sheets of drawing paper and charcoal or soft thick drawing pencils. Video footage showing a built environment. Clipboards, adult help

Resources needed for Lesson 3

Boxes which can be opened out and are shaped like the following: a triangular prism; a hexagonal prism; a pyramid. Triangular prism-shaped boxes, enough for one between two, scissors, glue and sugar paper. Copymaster 15, Homework Copymaster 16

Teaching the lessons

Lesson 1

Key questions

Can you describe this shape to me?

How many faces, edges, corners has this shape?

Vocabulary

Triangular prism, pyramid, base, vertex, face, edge, corner

Introduction 10min

Hold up a picture showing roofs, and point out the shapes of these. Draw one of them shaped like a triangular prism on the board. Tell the children that this shape is called a triangular prism. Ask them why they think triangular comes into the name. Then show the children the picture of the pyramids and ask the children what these are called. Write the words triangular prism and pyramid on the board.

Activities 35min

Ask the children to look carefully at their triangular prism-shaped box and write down all the things they

can say about it. Give them about 5 minutes and then bring the class together.

Ask the groups in turn to add something about the prism shape to a list of characteristics which you, the teacher, compile. Check that the list includes the following: five faces, six corners, three faces rectangular, the other two triangular.

Ask the children to use what they have learned in order to complete **Copymaster 14**.

Closing the lesson 5min

Show the children a hexagonal prism. Ask a child to come out and talk through the features of this shape.

Assessment

Child performance	Teacher action
Cannot name the features of prisms and pyramids	Give the children support in handling and talking about these shapes
Lacks confidence in tackling these shapes	Give more practice in activities like those in this lesson
Has sound concepts of these shapes	Move on to the next lesson

Lesson 2

Key questions

Can you point to a prism shape for me?

How do you know that is a prism?

Vocabulary

Prism, triangular, edge, slope, rectangle, triangle

Introduction `5min`

▦ Tell the children they are going to be looking for and drawing triangular prisms they can find in the built environment. Place the children in groups with an accompanying adult, clipboards and drawing materials.

Activities `40min`

�335 Allow the children access to the grounds around the school and to other buildings in the neighbourhood. They should try to spot triangular prisms among the roof shapes and record what they see on large sheets of drawing paper using charcoal or soft thick drawing pencils.

▦ Lay out the children's drawings and allow everyone to look at them.

Closing the lesson `10min`

▦ Show the children some video footage showing a built environment. Every time a child calls 'stop' pause the video and allow them to point out on the screen the triangular prism they can see.

Assessment

Child performance	Teacher action
Cannot find prisms in the built environment	Give the children more opportunities to look for and talk about triangular prisms in the company of an adult
Needs help to identify prisms in some locations	Give more practice in doing activities like those in the lesson
Can find prisms easily	Move on to the next lesson

Lesson 3

Key questions

What is a 'net'?

What shape matches this net?

Vocabulary

Triangular prism, pyramid, base, vertex, face, edge, corner

Introduction `15min`

▦ Cut open a box which is shaped like a triangular prism. Show the children the shape, and draw it out on the board. Then repeat this activity for a hexagonal prism and a pyramid.

Activities `30min`

▦▦ Allow the children to cut open their own triangular prism box and stick down the opened box on a piece of sugar paper.

▮ Ask the children to complete **Copymaster 15**.

Closing the lesson `10min`

▦ Play a 'name that shape' game using a set of shape pictures and their names on flashcards. The pictures could be made up as shown below:

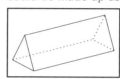
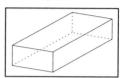
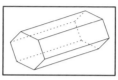
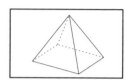
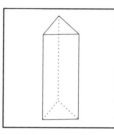
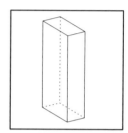
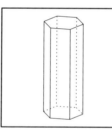
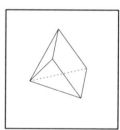

Rectangular prism (cuboid)	Triangular prism	Hexagonal prism	Pyramid

▦ Give the shape pictures out, one each to a group of children, and the shape name cards, one each, to another group of children. Ask them to find their 'partner' and stand in front of the class. All the remaining children can view the 'pairs' and check them out.

Assessment

Child performance	Teacher action
Cannot identify the nets of prisms and pyramids	Give individual help while the children open out shapes and look at the outcomes
Uncertain about nets	Give more matching practice
Can match nets to shapes	The learning targets for this theme have been met

HOMEWORK

Give the children the prism and pyramid puzzles sheet (**Copymaster 16**) to tackle and talk about at home.

THEME 7 # All about 3-D shapes

Learning targets

The children should be able to:

1 ➤➤ Identify the characteristics of a wide range of 3-D shapes using mathematical vocabulary

2 ➤➤ Identify by testing out, which shapes will roll, stack and fit together without spaces

3 ➤➤ Identify shapes made up from other 3-D shapes and make shape skeletons

Before you start

Subject knowledge

This theme brings together some of the things children may have learned about different shapes in other themes. There is a close relationship and interplay between the descriptions we make of 3-D and 2-D shapes. In looking at common features it is the case that the children should be isolating parts of the whole as they refine their understanding of shape.

Previous knowledge required

Everyday experience of shapes. Knowledge of some of the characteristics of some 3-D shapes.

Resources needed for Lesson 1

Mathematically correct and regular set of 3-D shapes including the following: cuboid, cube, sphere, cylinder, cone, triangular prism, hexagonal prism, pyramid. Irregular 3-D shapes (as many different ones as possible). Below are some suggestions, so that they can, if necessary, be made up before the lesson. Copymaster 17

Resources needed for Lesson 2

A box of 3-D shapes for each work group. The box should contain at least the following: cuboid, cube, sphere, cylinder, cone, triangular prism, hexagonal prism, pyramid. Copymasters 18 and 19

Resources needed for Lesson 3

Mosaic sets, coins, boxes that can be pushed together to make different shapes. Here are some suggestions:

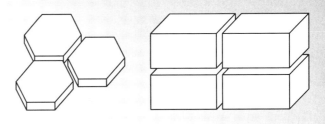

Copymaster 20, pack of matchboxes, cluster of triangular prisms

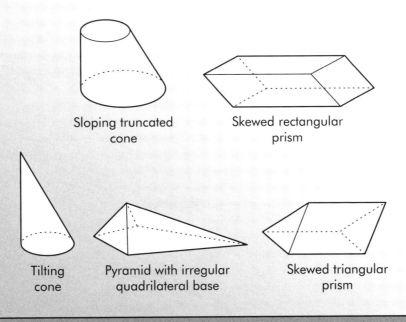

Sloping truncated cone

Skewed rectangular prism

Tilting cone

Pyramid with irregular quadrilateral base

Skewed triangular prism

Teaching the lessons

Lesson 1

Key questions

What is this shape called?

How do we write the name for this shape?

Which other shapes have the same number of faces, edges, corners as this shape?

Vocabulary

Shape names: cuboid, cube, sphere, cylinder, cone, triangular prism, rectangular prism, pyramid

Shape characteristics; face, edge, corner (vertex) apex, base (and words the children use)

Introduction `10 min`

 If the children have been working on shape in other sessions they should have an extensive knowledge and vocabulary. Check out the shape names, by holding up each of these shapes in turn (cuboid, cube, sphere, cylinder, cone, triangular prism, rectangular prism, pyramid) and asking what it is called. Then invite a child at a time to pick up each of the irregular shapes and name it. Place all the shapes around the room.

Activities `30 min`

Allow everyone to move around the room, visiting all the shapes that appear on **Copymaster 17** and noting their features.

 As a class, work through the Copymaster, checking out that everyone agrees about the attributes of the shapes.

Closing the lesson `15 min`

 Play 'I am thinking of a shape'. Describe the characteristics of a shape to the children and see how quickly they can say what the shape is called. Try this several times and then invite a child to have a turn at describing a shape.

Assessment

Child performance	Teacher action
Cannot identify the characteristics of a wide range of 3-D shapes	Give the children more practical experience of handling shapes, modelling with shapes and talking about shapes
Can talk about shapes but needs practice in using vocabulary	Engage the children in discussions about shapes
Adept at using mathematical language to describe shapes.	Move on to the next lesson

Lesson 2 ②

Key questions

Will this shape roll? Try it.

Will this one stack up?

Does this fit with other shapes like it?

Vocabulary

Cuboid, cube, sphere, cylinder, cone. triangular prism, rectangular prism, pyramid

Introduction `5 min`

Show the children **Copymaster 18** and talk through what they will be doing

Activities `40 min`

Using their box of shapes the children should try to answer all the questions on Copymaster 18. Each child can make their own record, but the group work enables them to discuss their answers.

Following the group work invite the children to think about the puzzles on **Copymaster 19** and see if they can respond to them.

Closing the lesson `10 min`

Ask the children for some of their responses to the puzzles on Copymaster 19 and discuss them with the class.

Assessment

Child performance	Teacher action
Cannot identify by testing out, which shapes will roll, stack and fit together without spaces	Allow the children many practical sessions with shapes before repeating this and other lessons in this section
Can work with shapes but lacks confidence	Give more practice at the kinds of activities shown in this lesson
Makes predictions and judgements about shapes with ease	Move on to the next lesson

Lesson 3 ③

Key questions

If we put several shapes like this together, what shape would we make?

If this shape was cut here what shapes would that make?

Vocabulary

Cuboid, cube, sphere, cylinder, cone, triangular prism, rectangular prism, pyramid

Introduction `5 min`

 Show the children the triangular prism boxes that push together to make a hexagonal prism like the following:

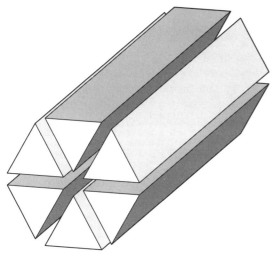

Tell the children that they are going to be looking at puzzles like this.

Activities 40 min

👤 Consulting the sample boxes when they need to, the children should try to complete **Copymaster 20**.

👥 Give each work group the name of one of the following shapes: cuboid, cube, triangular prism, rectangular prism, pyramid, and ask them to make a 'skeleton' using the plastic straws and Plasticine® blobs.

Closing the lesson 10 min

🔲 Allow the groups to look at one another's efforts at making skeletons. Point out that shapes do not need to be regular (thus a pyramid which is lopsided but has straight edges in its skeleton is still a pyramid).

Assessment

Child performance	Teacher action
Cannot detect 3-D shapes made up from other shapes or make shape 'skeletons'	The children need copious practical experience of shapes before repeating these lessons
Needs more practice at this work	Repeat the lessons in this theme
Can visualise and break down shapes and make 'skeletons'	The learning targets for this theme have been met

HOMEWORK

The children can choose a favourite 3-D shape, and explore how this shape is used in toys, buildings, sci-fi, ancient worlds, and stories.

Investigations

- Using a wide variety of found objects, design and make representational models.
- Using different 3-D objects make a range of prints that use the differing features of shape, texture and size.

- Make a container display getting the children to bring in any containers that they feel have interesting shapes.
- Explore a variety of containers in order to make statements about their similarities and differences. For example, use sand, water, or rice to compare how much containers will hold.

Assessment

- Order a given set of objects in respect of size.
- Order a given set of objects on an attribute elected by the child.

- Name some of the shapes made by the faces of given objects.
- Name some 3-D shapes.

2-D SHAPES

Whilst it is the case that everyday objects are 3-D, young children do encounter a wide variety of 'flat' patterns and illustrations. These range from patterns of floor and wall tiles to pictures and patterns printed in books. It is essential that youngsters get lots of practical opportunity to engage in free play with 2-D shapes. This play can be supported by the provision of a range of templates that (whilst being actually 3-D) give the child squares, rectangles, triangles and circles to manipulate and arrange in a wide variety of patterns. To these can be added flannelgraph shapes and sticker books with reusable plastic stickers. As they acquire more fine motor skills then the use of gummed shapes and stamps for printing can further extend their appreciation of the features of common 2-D shapes. This will include simple tessellation of, for example, squares of the same size but perhaps different colours. At this stage a wide variety of opportunities can be given and positively utilised. For example, the production of collage, and the making of friezes, banners and decorations. Once the children are competent and confident, the use of cutting and folding can be added to their repertoire of 2-D shape exploration. The demand of language and its use in mathematical settings continues to be of the utmost importance. As soon as the children start to identify 2-D shapes by their characteristics they should be using the appropriate names. This applies to all of the other shapes they encounter and recognise. Also they should be developing language that relates to the orientation of shapes and, in this process, becoming clear about what are 'real' and what are spurious characteristics of particular shapes. For example they should be developing the use and understanding of the terms 'horizontal' and 'vertical', and they should appreciate that a triangle is that regardless of whether it is standing on a side or a corner.

Allied to a developing understanding of the characteristics of 2-D shape (for example numbers of sides and corners) is the appreciation of aspects of symmetry. Indeed shapes such as the square and the equilateral triangle are often used in pattern making by young children, as they have an instinctive appreciation of their symmetries and the ways in which they might be juxtaposed. Linked to all of this understanding is the transfer of ideas between their knowledge of 2-D shapes and 3-D shapes.

Flat shapes

Learning targets

The children should be able to:

1 ➡➤ Sort and describe flat shapes

2 ➡➤ Print, draw and replicate polygons

3 ➡➤ Make shapes on a geoboard or with geostrips and record them and explore the use of dotty paper

Before you start

Subject knowledge

This, the first theme in the section, is intended to map onto children's first formal experiences with 2-D shapes. The children will have had copious everyday experience but may have had limited opportunities to focus on these shapes or articulate their own ideas. Shape names are not a priority in this theme because the children should be developing concepts about features of shapes.

Previous knowledge required

Everyday experiences and play with shapes

Resources needed for Lesson 1

A box containing a collection of polygons cut from card, for each work group. The box should contain at least 30 shapes, including the following: triangles, irregular quadrilaterals, squares, rectangles, irregular shapes with five, seven, eight, nine and ten straight sides, regular pentagons, regular hexagons. A sorting tray, Venn circles or large sheets of rough paper on which sets can be marked. Copymaster 21

Resources needed for Lesson 2

Extra adult help to supervise the art activities would be helpful. Card templates of shapes (those used in Lesson 1 are fine). Drawing paper, pencils, crayons and felt-tipped pens. Resources to make prints. These can, for example, include the following: polystyrene or plastic trays like those used to pack fresh meat and fish. Foam sponge and scissors to cut it. Poster paint made up thicker than usual (the addition of washing up liquid can make cleaning surfaces afterwards easier). Card polygons, glued to small blocks of wood or card boxes thus :

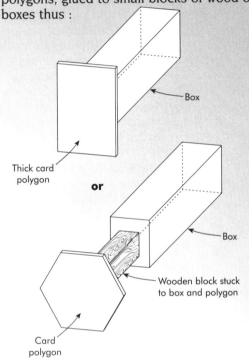

Thick card polygon

Box

or

Box

Card polygon

Wooden block stuck to box and polygon

Paper, hard plastic sheet and rollers, small trays with sand in them, PVA glue, lightweight card

Resources needed for Lesson 3

Geoboards (enough for half the class) and elastic bands, Copymaster 22, geostrips (enough for half the class), paper and pencils and crayons, square dotty and triangle dotty paper (General Copymasters A and B)

Homework: Copymaster 23

Teaching the lessons

Lesson 1 ❶

Key questions

Which shapes go with this one?

How many sides has this shape?

How many corners can you see?

Vocabulary

Match, sort, set, side, corner

Introduction ⌗⌗⌗ 10 min

▓ Take one of the group boxes of shapes. Tell the children that the box contains a collection of lots of shapes, and that some of them are similar. Hold up some example shapes so that the children can look at them.

Activities `30 min`

Give each group a box containing a collection of polygons cut from card. Invite the children to do the following:

- take turns at picking up a shape and describing it (each child should choose a different one)
- take turns at picking up a shape and finding another that is like it in some way (again each child should choose a different one)
- sort out all the shapes, putting them in sets

Ask the children to complete **Copymaster 21**, grouping the shapes according to their own criteria.

Closing the lesson `10 min`

Take some quadrilaterals out of one of the group boxes and lay them on the desk. Pick them up in turn and talk about how they are alike and how they are different. Assure the children that they all have four sides and are called quadrilaterals, but that some quadrilaterals also have special names; squares and rectangles being examples.

Assessment

Child performance	Teacher action
Cannot sort and describe flat shapes	With adult help give the children plenty of short practical sessions at sorting out shapes
Sorts shapes but not yet confident about features	Give more practice at activities like those in this lesson
Can sort and describe flat shapes	Move on to the next lesson

Lesson 2 ②

Key questions

Which shape is hardest to draw around? Why do you think that is?

Can you print a row of shapes the same?

Can you print a row where all the shapes are different?

Can you make a print and then turn the shape through a half a turn and print again? Now can you turn it a quarter turn and print again?

How do the prints compare?

If you turn the shape right around does the print match the first one you did?

Vocabulary

Print, the same, different, turn, halfway, quarter turn

Introduction `5 min`

As this is to be a workshop session, the children need to be apprised of what is expected of them in all the activities, and some rules about how to behave, when to clean up and so on. Walk the children around the room, explaining the main requirements in each activity. Then assign the groups to their first activity.

Activities `45 min`

Allow each group to attempt each of the activities in rotation.

Given card templates of 2-D shapes ask the children to practise drawing carefully around them. They can make patterns or pictures of their own choice.

Invite the children to make prints using the shape printing blocks. With adult questioning they can try repeat patterns, and turning a shape before printing again and again. If hard plastic sheets and rollers are available, the children can roll out some paint, draw a freehand pattern of shape outlines and then lay a sheet of paper onto the paint to make a record of their work.

There are two activities here involving sand. Some children can draw outlines of shapes in level sand, and then shake the tray gently before drawing another shape. Others can paste a freehand shape outline onto card. If sand is shaken onto the glue, it will adhere and when dry can provide a texture outline.

Closing the lesson `5 min`

Hold up some of the work the children have done so that they can comment on the shapes they see. After the lesson, mount a display of some of the best examples.

Assessment

Child performance	Teacher action
Cannot follow instructions to print, draw and replicate polygons	Give the children small highly structured tasks with frequent feedback so that they follow instructions better
Enjoys the work with shapes but lacks precision	Give the children more practice without time limitations so that they can produce work of a higher standard
Produces good work related to polygons	Move on to the next lesson

Lesson 3 ③

Key questions

Can you make shapes like this?

Can you make a similar bigger shape?

Can you make a shape with three, four, five... sides?

How many different shapes can you draw using dotty paper?

Vocabulary

Polygon, quadrilateral, straight, side

Introduction `5 min`

If the children have not met them before, show them the geoboards and the geostrips strips and point out how shapes can be made with them.

2-D SHAPES

Activities $\boxed{\text{40min}}$

 Allow two groups of children to try out some geoboard shapes. If you wish, they can make the shapes shown on **Copymaster 22**. Then they can swop about with the groups using geostrips.

 Ask the children to work as a group or in pairs or threes to make up some shapes with the geostrips

Give each child a piece of square dotty or triangle dotty paper (**General Copymaster A** or **B**) and ask them to create as many shapes as they can using the paper.

Closing the lesson $\boxed{\text{5min}}$

Make a triangle, a square and a hexagon from geostrips and talk about them, giving the children their names.

Assessment

Child performance	Teacher action
Cannot make shapes on a geoboard or with geostrips	Give the children adult support in shape making with this apparatus
Makes shapes but uncertain about their features	Allow the children to make shapes and talk about their work
Can make shapes and record them on dotty paper	The learning targets for this theme have been met

HOMEWORK

Give the children **Copymaster 23** where there is a shape maze and a set of challenges for them to try at home.

Rectangles and squares

Learning targets

The children should be able to:

1 ➥ Identify rectangles and squares
2 ➥ Know the angles and other features of rectangles and squares
3 ➥ Explore parts of rectangles and squares

Before you start

Subject knowledge

The children should, after working on this theme, know the features of rectangles and squares thoroughly and be confident about working with them. Some children will still see these as distinct named shapes and will not be at a stage where they understand that the square is a special form of rectangle. It is important, therefore, to take the opportunity to focus in on sides and corners on a regular basis as this will help with firm foundations for future categorisation.

Previous knowledge required

Some experience of work with 2-D shapes, especially contact with quadrilaterals.

Resources needed for Lesson 1

Adult help, access to parts of the school building. A collection of polygons including squares and rectangles of a range of sizes (a box of these is required for each workgroup). Copymaster 24

Resources needed for Lesson 2

Card templates of squares and rectangles, drawing paper, rough paper. Copymaster 25

Resources needed for Lesson 3

Card templates of squares and rectangles, sticky paper and scissors, sugar paper, dotty paper (General Copymaster A), Copymaster 26

Teaching the lessons

Lesson 1 ①

Key questions

What is this shape called?
Which of these are squares?
Can you point to a rectangle here?

Vocabulary

Polygon, quadrilateral, square, rectangle

Introduction 10min

Remind the children that they are studying flat shapes. Draw the outline of an irregular four-sided shape on the board. Ask the children how many sides and how many corners it has. Tell the children that all flat shapes with four sides are called quadrilaterals. Some of them are rather special and so have special names, and in this lesson they will be looking at two of these, a rectangle and a square. Draw a rectangle on the board. Ask the children what it is called and confirm its name. Then do the same with a square.

Activities 40min

Remind the children that everything in our world is 3-D (that is has three dimensions, including thickness), but that we find it useful to look at the flat parts of shapes and give them names. Point to a box or drawer front and draw around the front face, telling the children that this face is a rectangle. Ask them to point to and describe more rectangles they can see in the room. Examples might include the surface of a plank or wood-block in the floor, the front of a book, the side of a bookshelf.

Ask each group with adult help, to find three different things in the school building that have faces that are rectangles, and report back in a whole class session.

Invite each group to sort out from their sets of shapes, the squares and rectangles. Check each group's sort.

Ask the children to colour the sets on **Copymaster 24**.

Closing the lesson 5min

Confirm the names of the square and rectangle and write these on the board. Hold up a series of squares and rectangles in random order and ask the children to point to and call out the appropriate name.

Assessment

Child performance	Teacher action
Cannot identify rectangles and squares	Give the children individual adult support in 'playing'

with card shapes, before repeating the activities of this lesson

Hesitant in identification of squares and rectangles | Give the child more practice in activities like those in this lesson

Can identify rectangles and squares with confidence | Move on to the next lesson

characteristics of some shapes and ask them to draw a rough freehand outline. Here are some suggestions:

- a shape with three straight sides
- a shape with four corners
- a shape with two pairs of matching sides and four corners the same
- a shape with five sides
- a shape with four corners all the same, and four sides all the same length.

Assessment

Child performance	Teacher action
Does not know features of rectangles and squares	Allow the children to handle and draw around card templates, and talk about the shapes they have drawn
Is unsure about the features of rectangles and squares	Give more practice in activities like those in this lesson
Knows the features of rectangles and squares	Move on to the next lesson

Lesson 2 ②

Key questions

What is this angle called?

How many corners has a rectangle?

What can we say about the angles at the corners?

What do we know about the sides of a square?

Vocabulary

Rectangle, square, corner, side, right angle, straight, matching, pair

Introduction `15min`

▦ Draw a large rectangle and a large square on the board (make these accurate drawings). Inside each one write the characteristics of these shapes as the children call them out. Check that the lists are as follows:

4 sides the same 4 corners the same	4 sides - 2 matching pairs 4 corners the same

Activities `35min`

⚫⚫ Give each group a range of templates of squares and rectangles of different sizes, and invite each child, within their group, to use these shapes to make a picture. They should draw around the shapes. This will enable the children to show the shapes in a range of orientations.

▦ Using the picture they have made, invite the children to choose one rectangle and one square in their picture. Using the pictures on the board, show the children how to mark in the right angles and the matching sides on their shape, thus:

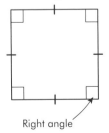

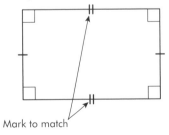

Right angle   Mark to match

▣ The children can record what they now know about squares and rectangles on **Copymaster 25**.

Closing the lesson `5min`

▦ Give each child a piece of rough paper. Call out the

Lesson 3 ③

Key questions

Can you find a matching half for this? What shape is made?

How many different squares and rectangles can you make on this dotty paper?

Vocabulary

Corner, side, straight, fraction, half, match

Introduction `10min`

▦ Draw a rectangle on the board. Show the children how it can be cut into two equal pieces in a variety of ways. Here are some examples:

Activities `40min`

👥 Taking a square and a rectangle template, the children should each draw around both on coloured sugar paper, cut each shape into two equal parts and then ask their partner to try re-making the shapes.

▣ **Copymaster 26** presents the child with matching challenges involving squares and rectangles.

▣ Give each child a sheet of dotty paper (**General Copymaster A**) and ask them to draw as many different-sized squares and rectangles as they can.

Closing the lesson

Show the children, using dots drawn on the board, that we can, for example, draw a square using four dots, the next biggest takes in 9 dots and the next 16 (this is the pattern of square numbers) and that we can make different rectangles taking in the same number of dots. Examples are shown here:

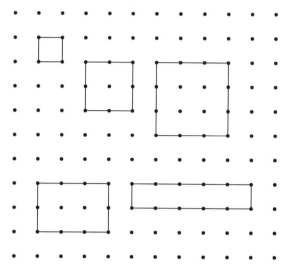

Assessment

Child performance
Finds difficulty in exploring parts of rectangles and squares

Teacher action
Allow the children to 'play' at drawing around and cutting out shapes in a number of sessions. Try for increasing precision and allow the children to talk about what they are doing

Needs to develop more confidence

Rehearse these skills and concepts again by repeating the activities in this lesson

Can explore and articulate what they find out about parts of squares and rectangles

The learning targets for this theme have been met

HOMEWORK

Give each child a piece of sticky paper and a sheet of paper to mount their work on. Ask them to find something at home to use as a template for a rectangle and a square. They should draw around them and cut them out of sticky paper. They can cut each shape in half and stick it down on the page so that the pieces do not quite butt up against one another, like this:

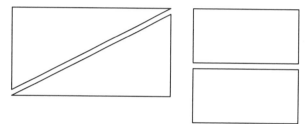

If you wish they can write the name of the shape and its parts.

Learning targets

The children should be able to:

1 ➡➤ Recognise, print and draw circles

2 ➡➤ Use templates, spirographs and computer graphics to make circle patterns

3 ➡➤ Begin to explore fractions of a circle

Before you start

Subject knowledge

The circle is an exceptional shape with unique characteristics. Whilst a circle is very familiar it is difficult to define its characteristics. At this stage what is important is recognition of circles and experience in looking at dimensions, relationships with other shapes and where we find and use circles. Definition can be left until much later.

Previous knowledge required

Everyday experience of circular and spherical shapes.

Resources needed for Lesson 1

A collection of card templates including circles, ovoid shapes and ellipses. Polystyrene or plastic trays like those used to pack fresh meat and fish. Foam sponge and scissors to cut it Poster paint in two colours, made up thicker than usual (the addition of washing up liquid can make cleaning surfaces afterwards easier) Card cylinders, corks and bottle tops with which to make prints. Copymaster 27

Resources needed for Lesson 2

Card circle templates, Spirograph® sets. Home-

made spirographs, made up as follows:

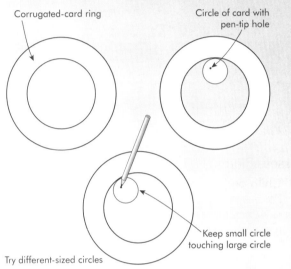

Corrugated-card ring

Circle of card with pen-tip hole

Keep small circle touching large circle

Try different-sized circles

Computer with graphics/shapes package if appropriate. Copymaster 28

Resources needed for Lesson 3

Circles of tissue or sugar paper (enough for every child to have three). Template card circles, half circles and quarter circles. Drawing paper. Copymaster 29

Homework: Copymaster 30

Teaching the lessons

Lesson 1 ①

Key questions

Which are the circles here?

What do we mean by 'sit in a circle', 'draw around this shape', 'roundabout'?

Vocabulary

Circle, round, around, oval, ellipse

Introduction 5 min

▦ Set out a series of large cut out shapes including a circle, an oval and an ellipse. Hold each up in turn and tell the children what they are called. Write their names up on the board. Hold up each again and ask

the children to draw the shape using their pointing finger in the air.

Activities 40 min

♣♣ For the first activity each group needs a collection of card templates including circles, ovoid shapes and ellipses. They should all look carefully at them and place them in sets, count them, talk about their similarities and differences, and mention the locations where they have seen shapes like this before.

♣♣ Ask groups of children to try printing circles and make repeat patterns. The group should work out a pattern or order before starting work. Confirm that the paint should not be applied with a brush, and that the action of 'press in paint, press on paper' is fundamental to printing.

👤 Invite the children to identify and colour the circles on **Copymaster 27**.

Closing the lesson `10 min`

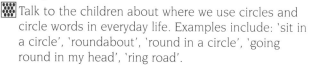Talk to the children about where we use circles and circle words in everyday life. Examples include: 'sit in a circle', 'roundabout', 'round in a circle', 'going round in my head', 'ring road'.

Assessment

Child performance	Teacher action
Cannot recognise, print and draw circles	Give individual practical experience with circle shapes
Works with circles but lacks confidence	Give more practice in the activities in this lesson
Can recognise, print and draw circles	Move on to the next lesson

---

Lesson 2 ②

Key questions

Can you draw a circle using this card shape?

Can you make a smaller/larger circle?

Vocabulary

Circle, circular, smaller, larger, around, round

Introduction `5 min`

Show and demonstrate the commercially produced Spirograph® and the home-made ones.

Activities `40 min`

Invite the children to practice drawing around card circle templates.

Ask the children to look on while everyone has a turn at drawing circles using the Spirograph® sets or the home-made circle aids.

Working on the computer, a pair at a time, the children can produce images of circles.

Closing the lesson `10 min`

Give the children **Copymaster 28**. Point out that the things in the picture are three-dimensional but the drawing is flat. In the flat drawing how many circles can they see?

Assessment

Child performance	Teacher action
Cannot make circle patterns	Allow the children, both in school and at home, to use templates and card circle aids to 'play' at circle drawing
Tries to make circles but needs more practice	Give the children more practice at this kind of drawing
Can make circle patterns	Move on to the next lesson

Lesson 3 ③

Key questions

Can you find another shape like this?

What can we make with two of these shapes?

Can you spot the quarter circle? Which of these shapes do we need to make a whole circle?

Vocabulary

Shape, circle, half, quarter, whole, fraction, sector, sixth

Introduction `5 min`

Assemble examples of a large whole circle, a semi-circle and a quarter circle. Hold up each in turn and tell the children what it is called.

Activities `40 min`

Give each child three circles of tissue or sugar paper. Show them how to fold the first one into two halves. ask them to open it out and examine the halves. Point out that each part or fraction is a half circle. Now ask them to fold the next circle into four parts, by making two folds. Again they can examine the resulting quarter circles. Finally show them how to fold in half and then make two more folds to cut each half into three. When opened out each sector is a sixth of the whole.

Give each group some card templates of circles, half circles and quarter circles. Ask them to share the shapes, allowing each child to draw and label their own.

Ask the children to complete **Copymaster 29**.

Closing the lesson `5 min`

Give the children mental challenges like the following:

'How many circles can I make from four half circles?'

'One and a half circles – how many quarter circles are there?'

Assessment

Child performance	Teacher action
Does not have a concept of fractions of a circle	Allow the children, with adult help, to make up and take apart circles from circle pieces and talk about their work
Beginning to master ideas about parts of a circle	Give the children more practice at working with circles
Has good mastery of ideas about fractions of a circle	The learning targets for this theme have been met

---

HOMEWORK

Using **Copymaster 30** the children can make and play with their own drawing aid. (They may need adult help in cutting the card.)

THEME 11 | Triangles and hexagons

Learning targets

The children should be able to:

1 ➤➤ Draw triangles and cut other shapes into triangles
2 ➤➤ Use geostrips and dotty paper to explore triangles
3 ➤➤ Identify a hexagon and explore its features

Before you start

Subject knowledge

The work in this theme is closely connected to that in Unit 4 on angle. Triangles and hexagons are related in that equilateral forms of each tessellate and regular hexagons can be made from equilateral triangles. A common mistake that children can make with the characteristics of triangles is that they can come to believe that triangles always 'stand' on a flat, horizontal base. This is because we often depict triangles in this way. It is a good idea, therefore, to consciously vary the orientation of different triangles so that the children focus on the really key features: namely numbers and length of sides; and numbers and 'shapes' of corners.

Previous knowledge required

Everyday knowledge of 2-D shapes

Resources needed for Lesson 1

Templates of a range of straight-sided 2-D shapes, including triangles, quadrilaterals, pentagons and hexagons. Sugar paper, scissors and glue. Copymaster 31

Resources needed for Lesson 2

Geoboards and geostrips (enough for half the class to be working on). Triangle dotty paper (General Copymaster B)

Resources needed for Lesson 3

Card templates of hexagons, both regular and irregular. Rulers. Mats made up from Copymaster 32

Teaching the lessons

Lesson 1 ①

Key questions

Which of these are triangles?

How many triangles can you cut this shape into?

Vocabulary

Triangle, quadrilateral, pentagon, hexagon, diagonal

Introduction   5 min

▓ Hold up a card triangle. Ask the children what it is called. Confirm that it is called a triangle. Ask the children to describe it. Then hold up a triangle of a different kind (with angles of different sizes) and ask the children to describe that. Point out that the characteristics of all triangles are three straight sides and three corners.

Activities   40 min

◆◆ Give each group a collection of card templates. Include triangles, quadrilaterals, pentagons and hexagons. Ask them to sort out the triangles from the rest of the shapes. They can then take one of the other shapes each, draw around it, and then using a

ruler, draw lines to cut the shape into triangles. They can colour each triangle a different colour. Here are some examples:

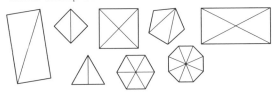

▓▓ Give each pair of children a triangle template. They can draw around it and cut it out several times using sugar paper. Ask them to stick the shapes down, turning each in a different position from the one before, and sticking each onto sugar paper. The results may look something like this:

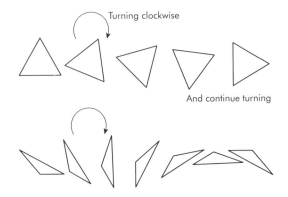

Turning clockwise

And continue turning

Point out that these are all triangles, no matter which way up they sit.

 Invite the children to complete **Copymaster 31**.

Closing the lesson   `5min`

Hold up some of the shapes the children have drawn in the first activity and point out how many triangles have been made. If appropriate, give the whole shape name (like pentagon and hexagon) and also talk about what a diagonal is.

Assessment

Child performance	Teacher action
Cannot draw around triangles and cut other shapes into triangles	Give individual adult help in several sessions until the children are confident in drawing around and identifying triangles
Unsure about identifying all cases of a triangle	Move on to the next lesson and then review the children's confidence about triangles
Can work with triangles	Move on to the next lesson

Lesson 2   ②

Key questions

Can you point to a triangle here?

Can you make a bigger/smaller triangle?

How many triangles are there in your pattern?

Vocabulary

Triangle, smaller, larger

Introduction   `5min`

Revise the characteristics of triangles with the children, reminding them of Lesson 1.

Activities   `40min`

Allow half the class, in their groups, to be making triangles using geoboards and geostrips. If they swop about after 10 minutes the children can all work with both kinds of apparatus. In the meantime the other half of the class can do the next activity

Ask the children to produce and replicate their own patterns of triangles on triangle dotty paper.

Closing the lesson   `10min`

Create an 'instant' display of the children's work, discussing what they have done with geoboard, geostrip and dotty patterns.

Assessment

Child performance	Teacher action
Has difficulty in using geoboards, geostrips and dotty paper to explore triangles	Allow the children many practical sessions with 2-D shapes and shape games
Needs more practical work with triangles	Give the children opportunities to work again on

activities like those in the previous two lessons

Confident in work with triangles	Move on to the next lesson

Lesson 3   ③

Key questions

What is the name of this shape?

Can you draw a hexagon?

How many sides/corners has a hexagon?

Vocabulary

Hexagon, side, corner

Introduction   `5min`

Hold up a regular hexagon, and ask the children what it is called. Confirm, with the help of the children, the name and features of a hexagon. Show the children some irregular hexagons and point out that these are indeed hexagons.

Activities   `40min`

Give each group a collection of hexagon templates, and allow the children to draw around the shapes and talk about them.

Each child can draw around a regular hexagon and then use a ruler to draw lines cutting it into other shapes.

Allow each group several sets of mats made up from **Copymaster 32**. They can lay these down to make a continuous pattern. Then ask all the children to take one or two mats and create a class pattern.

Closing the lesson   `5min`

Hold up one of the mats and point out to the children that the pattern on it is drawn so that it will join exactly with the pattern on another mat of the same kind. Invite the children to create a mat design for themselves in another lesson, or at home.

Assessment

Child performance	Teacher action
Cannot identify a hexagon	Give individual support to the children in learning shape names and features
Lacks confidence in identifying and exploring hexagons	Allow the children to repeat some of the activities involving hexagons
Confident in work with hexagons	The learning targets for this theme have been met

HOMEWORK

Give each child a copy of Copymaster 32 so that they can create their own set of mats. Invite them to trace off one of the hexagon outlines and make a mat design of their own. These can be brought to school, replicated and played with by all the children, before being added to class resources.

33

Patterns and tessellation

Learning targets

The children should be able to:

1 ➤➤ Use shapes in pattern making
2 ➤➤ Find shapes that fit together and make patterns
3 ➤➤ Explore tessellation

Before you start

Subject knowledge

The lessons here provide the children with the opportunities to investigate pattern-making in different cultures and to use shapes to create their own repeat patterns. They can also look specifically for shapes that fit together without spaces and try to create some of these patterns for themselves. In a sense the first part of this theme involves re-visiting work the children may have done in Theme 8, but that theme may have been tackled in their Reception year whereas this theme is intended for children with prodigious experience of work with shape and would be better attempted with Year 2 children.

Previous knowledge required

Everyday experience of shapes, names and features of 2-D shapes

Resources needed for Lesson 1

Resources to make prints: polystyrene or plastic trays like those used to pack fresh meat and fish. Foam sponge and scissors to cut it. Poster paint made up thicker than usual (the addition of washing up liquid can make cleaning surfaces afterwards easier). Card polygons, glued to small blocks of wood or card boxes, bottle tops, packaging, in fact any shape that can be used to make a print. Sets of 2-D shape templates (enough for each group to have one set) Copymaster 33

Resources needed for Lesson 2

Patterns and artefacts showing pattern from a wide variety of cultures. These could include the North American Indians and Ancient Greeks. Create a classroom display before the lesson begins. Access to patterns in the built environment, either in school or other local buildings. Extra adult help would be invaluable here. Charcoal, felt-tipped pens, paint and crayons

Resources needed for Lesson 3

Templates for squares and rectangles (with sides of at least 5cm), Drawing paper and scissors. Examples of the work of M. C. Escher would be useful. Copymaster 34

Teaching the lessons

Lesson 1 ①

Key questions

How does this pattern continue? What comes next?

Can you tell me about your pattern?

Vocabulary

Pattern, repeat, sequence (2-D shape names as they arise in the children's patterns)

Introduction 5min

▨ Remind the children that in mathematics a pattern involves regular repetition. Show the children examples involving the repeat of a shape, a colour, a position, a size. Tell them they should be thinking about these ideas while making their patterns in this lesson.

Activities 40min

▨ Allow a group to do their printing while the others pursue the other two activities, and then they can swop about. Ask the children to make their own repeat print, by pressing shapes into foam pads soaked in thick poster paint and then pressing the shape gently onto paper.

▨ Ask the children to draw around the templates to make a repeat pattern of shapes. Encourage the children to devise complex repeats, rather than doing a simple '1-1-1-1-1-1' pattern.

▨ Ask the children to complete **Copymaster 33**.

Closing the lesson 5min

▨ Invite the children to look around at some of the work done by their classmates. Point out some of the patterns created in their work.

Assessment

Child performance	Teacher action
Finds it hard to create repeat patterns	Show the children simple repeat patterns. Point out the repetition and ask them to predict what comes next. Cover patterns and reveal the items in an array one at a time, so that the children can see the pattern developing. Then move on as below
Needs practice in creating complex patterns	Give the child more opportunities to practice pattern making
Can create patterns with ease	Move on to the next lesson

Lesson 2

Key questions

Can you see a pattern here?

What shapes are in this pattern?

Vocabulary

Specialised vocabulary related to the display, names for 2-D shapes seen in the environment as faces (for example, bricks, tiles etc.), fit together

Introduction　10min

 Point out some of the items on display and talk about the patterns to be seen, including especially those patterns where shapes fit together without any spaces in between.

Activities　30min

Using items or patterns from the classroom display the children should copy and extend the patterns, using a range of media. These could include, charcoal, felt-tipped pens, paint and crayon.

With adult help allow the children to go and look for patterns of shape in brickwork, flooring, wallpapers and other parts of the building or other local buildings.

Closing the lesson　10min

 Choose some of the work the children have done on pattern to hold up, before placing it on display.

Assessment

Child performance	Teacher action
Cannot recognise patterns where shapes fit together	Invite the children to look at patterns with adult guidance, for a few minutes every day until they can detect them for themselves
Hesitant in talking about patterns	Give the children more practice in pattern-making
Adept at pattern recognition and replication	Move on to the next lesson

Lesson 3　

Key questions

Do these shapes fit together without spaces in between?

Can you lay out some shapes that fit together?

Vocabulary

Fit together, spaces, tessellate, tessellation

Introduction　10min

 Remind the children of the work they have done in identifying patterns around them, where the faces of, for example, bricks fit together with no spaces in between. Point out that when shapes do this we say they tessellate. Tell the children that they are going to make patterns without spaces in this lesson.

Activities　40min

Give every child a template that is a square or a rectangle, along with at least two large sheets of drawing paper. On the first sheet ask them to draw around their shape at least 6 times, making sure that the shapes are touching along at least one side. The resulting patterns may look something like this:

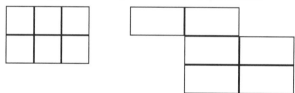

Now ask the children to draw around their shape and cut it out. They can then cut a piece out of one side of the shape and stick it onto the other side as shown on **Copymaster 34**.

Closing the lesson　10min

Using a large card shape, make a tessellating picture on the board, or hold up some reproductions of the work of M. C. Escher, to show the children the elaborate tessellations.

Assessment

Child performance	Teacher action
Cannot make tessellating patterns	Allow the children to look for and make (with shaped jigsaws, floor mosaics and card shapes) patterns where there are no spaces between the pieces
Struggles to make tessellating patterns	Needs more practice in making tessellations
Has skills and ideas in making tessellations	The learning targets for this theme have been met

HOMEWORK

Give the children copies of Copymaster 34 to take home. Here they are asked to replicate and invent their own pictures in a tessellating pattern.

Reflective symmetry

Learning targets

The children should be able to:

1 ➡➤ Play with folding, cutting and painting to make pictures with matching halves

2 ➡➤ Explore left and right and 'match' in things around us

3 ➡➤ Study symmetry in 2-D shapes

Before you start

Subject knowledge

This is a phenomenon that children will already be familiar with in everyday life. There are many things in our world, including ourselves, that show close similarity, if not complete match between the halves. In this theme the children will be enabled to use their everyday observations and to hone these so that they can find out which of the 2-D shapes they have worked on have axes of symmetry.

Previous knowledge required

Everyday experience of match, pairs, left and right and patterns

Resources needed for Lesson 1

Sugar paper and painting paper, and paper which is not too absorbent. Scissors and poster paints. Copymaster 35

Resources needed for Lesson 2

Display of objects from the natural world. Here are some examples: leaves, cones, fruits, bi-valve shells, pictures of humans and other animals; also include some manufactured items where symmetry is apparent, for example a pair of shorts, a flower vase with two handles, a basket. Plane mirrors (enough for one for each pair of children). Copymaster 36

Resources needed for Lesson 3

Templates of 2-D shapes including both regular and irregular examples of at least the following: triangles, quadrilaterals (including squares and rectangles), pentagons, hexagons. Copymaster 37

Teaching the lessons

Lesson 1

Key questions

What do you think the shape will look like when it is opened out?

Can you fold the paper and cut a shape like this?

Can you see the matching halves?

Vocabulary

Shape, halve, half, match

Introduction [10 min]

Take a piece of paper and fold it down the middle. Cut a shape along the unfolded side and open it out. Point out to the children that the shape has halves that match. Describe the activities that they will be doing, emphasising that they will be looking for match in their pictures.

Activities [35 min]

Allow a group at a time to do this and the next activity while the remainder of the class work on the Copymaster. Give the children access to paper which is not too absorbent, and poster paints. They should fold their paper crisply along the centre line and then place paint splodges to one side of the fold. When the paper is folded down onto the paint and pressed and rubbed gently some of the paint is transferred to the paper to the other side of the fold. When opened out the picture should demonstrate matching halves. If this is appropriate these can be called butterfly pictures.

Show the children how to fold lightweight paper pieces and then cut a shape or notches out of the folded paper, so that shapes are made with matching halves. Each child can do several of these. Strips of paper can be folded concertina fashion, as shown here:

The paper here does need to be very thin, or the children will find it difficult to cut through several layers at once.

Invite the children to explore the pictures and patterns on **Copymaster 35**.

Closing the lesson `5min`

Hold up some examples of the children's work and talk through the images on the Copymaster with them.

Assessment

Child performance	Teacher action
Finds it difficult to make pictures with matching halves	Give the children opportunities to do more folding and cutting, and discuss with an adult what they are doing
Needs more practice in producing and detecting pictures with matching halves	Give more practice in activities like those in this lesson
Can easily make and identify pictures with matching halves	Move on to the next lesson

Lesson 2 ②

Key questions

Can you point to something that has matching halves?

Where could we draw a line on this to show a similar part of the picture on each side?

Vocabulary

Shape, halve, half, match

Introduction `10min`

▨ Draw the children's attention to the display put up before the lesson and ask them to note that some things around us have matching halves and that we ourselves have halves which broadly match. Talk to them about 'left' and 'right'.

Activities `40min`

⚇ Allow a group at a time to do this activity while the rest of the class get on with the other activities. Allow the children to inspect, handle and draw some of the things on display.

👥 Give each pair of children a plane safety mirror, and allow them to explore things around the room. They should take turns to stand the mirror up and look into it as shown here.

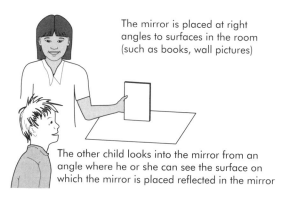

The mirror is placed at right angles to surfaces in the room (such as books, wall pictures)

The other child looks into the mirror from an angle where he or she can see the surface on which the mirror is placed reflected in the mirror

👤 Ask the children to complete **Copymaster 36**.

Closing the lesson `5min`

▦ Take the children to look in a cloakroom or other large mirror. Using a child as a model, point out to them that when the child puts up his or her left hand, it looks as though it is the right hand in the reflection.

Assessment

Child performance	Teacher action
Finds it difficult to detect 'match' in things around us	Give the children individual support in examining and talking about objects around them
Needs more opportunities to explore 'match' and left and right	Give more practice in work on symmetry
Can locate 'match' and identify left and right	Move on to the next lesson

Lesson 3 ③

Key questions

Which of these shapes are symmetrical?

Where should we put the lines of symmetry here?

Vocabulary

Names for shapes, symmetry, symmetrical, line symmetry, mirror symmetry

Introduction `5min`

▨ Draw a rectangle on the board. Draw a line across the rectangle and point out to the children that it can be sliced into two matching halves. We could put a mirror along the halfway line and the reflection would match what is in front of the mirror. Tell the children that we say a rectangle shows mirror or line symmetry. Draw a line across the rectangle in the other direction, and show that it also has a line of symmetry in this direction. Tell the children they will be looking for the lines of symmetry in a number of 2-D shapes.

Activities `45min`

⚇ Give each group a similar collection of 2-D shape templates. Invite the group to decide for each shape in turn, whether it shows symmetry and how many lines of symmetry it shows.

▦ Bring the class together and talk about the outcomes of their discussions about the shapes. Draw on the board: an equilateral triangle, a square, a rectangle and a hexagon. Then ask the children to draw around templates of these shapes and with a ruler draw in the lines of symmetry.

👥 Using their drawings of the shapes the children should place the plane safety mirror on their lines of symmetry and confirm that the reflections do indeed match what is in front of the mirror.

👤 Ask the children to complete **Copymaster 37** and then check their drawings using a plane safety mirror.

Closing the lesson | 5 min |

▦ Draw some more unusual shapes on the board. There are some examples here (where lines of symmetry are drawn in – though these should not appear until the children have given their own ideas):

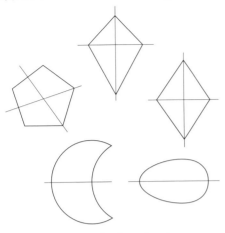

Ask the children whether the shapes are symmetrical, and where they think the lines should be drawn.

Assessment

Child performance	Teacher action
Finds the concept of symmetry difficult to understand	Give the children copious opportunities to play with plane safety mirrors, then repeat the lessons in this theme
Needs more practice in order to be confident	Allow more practice in activities like those in this lesson
Detects and describes symmetry in shapes	The learning targets for this theme have been met.

HOMEWORK

Invite the children to make a little 'play' book to do with symmetry. For example, they can draw half a face, so that a plane safety mirror can be placed at the edge of the picture in order to create a whole face.

Investigations

- Make class books of the triangle, the square and so on.
- Make symmetrical prints by folding painted sheets in half. Develop this to use two folds to produce symmetrical patterns.

- Explore a given set of 3-D shapes and identify some of the 2-D shapes that can be seen. Make a display that links these using objects, pictures and the appropriate written words.
- Fold and tear paper to make symmetrical shapes.
- Using templates, printing stamps, gummed paper and so on produce a display of symmetrical patterns designed and made by the children.

Assessment

- Using two congruent triangles the children should make as many different shapes as they can. Can they name any of the shapes they make?

- Using geoboards the children should be able to make named 2-D shapes. They should also be challenged to make a variety of four- and six-sided shapes.

POSITION AND MOVEMENT

As with so much of the work in mathematics, the use of language is key to the child's genuine understanding of what we mean by position and the fact that we often use position as a snapshot of a movement. The children need in the first instance, to recognise position as the location of an object, person, or place. The vocabulary here will include above, below, beneath, next to, inside and outside. The quantification of position comes later. However, when the children do move to the use of quantities such as the use of co-ordinates to describe position, it is essential that they have already understood the vocabulary of position. This also includes concepts about the vertical and the horizontal as these are important judgements about position when it comes to further work on shape and angle.

There are two ways in which we use position descriptions, one being for static and the other for dynamic objects. Important for the latter is the development of ideas about angle. Angle can be seen as fixed, an example being a 'corner'. Thus for the mathematician the corner of the table has a fixed, static angle. However, in many other circumstances angle needs to be viewed as a measure of rotation and in relation to a complete rotation. When opening a book the pages are at an increasing angle. Opening a door gives the same effect, as does using a pair of scissors. This idea of movement around a hinge or fulcrum is very important. Early work in angle will generally be to do with fixed angles but as soon as it is viable children need to be introduced to the dynamic nature of angle.

Young children are developing a sense of self. It is therefore extremely valuable to make use of the children's wishes to sense the movement of their own bodies and their positions in relation to other people and objects. The PE or games lesson provides powerful opportunities to explore position and use appropriate vocabulary. There is also the chance to start to lay the foundations for understanding both static and dynamic positions and angles in these sessions.

Developing a vocabulary

Learning targets

The children should be able to:

1 ➤➤ Use a variety of appropriate words and terms to describe position

2 ➤➤ Investigate left and right

3 ➤➤ Explore and discuss turning movements

Before you start

Subject knowledge

In everyday life, we all make considerable use of our understanding and appreciation of shapes and spaces in our home-making, response to the built environment, in playing and watching sports and games, in finding our way, and in keeping safe. In order to be able to understand and share what we know about ourselves as 3-D beings in a 3-D world and the relationship of ourselves to others and the environment it is vital that we have the means to communicate our perceptions and reactions. To do this we need, from an early age, to lay down the foundations of a language of shapes, spaces and related ideas such as location, position, dimensions and movements. In this theme we introduce some key vocabulary that the children need to become familiar with.

Previous knowledge required

The children should have some of the vocabulary but their repertoire will be clearly affected by pre-school opportunities in such activities as constructing, painting and drawing, games, and tidying up.

Resources needed for Lesson 1

A toy spider, plastic bowl and spoon. 6 small items like the following: silver thimble, hair slide, sock, pencil with novelty top attached, small soft toy, mitten. Copymaster 38

Resources needed for Lesson 2

A display, showing a pair of socks, a pair of mittens, a pair of tights, a pair of slippers and a pair of trousers, all labelled with 'left' and 'right'. A pair of large-size hand-prints and footprints. Copymasters 39 and 40

Resources needed for Lesson 3

An open door, a cupboard door, a book, a child's spinning top, a pair of pliers, a rotary egg whisk, a plastic bottle with top, a pair of scissors, a toy car, a toy wheelbarrow and other things that turn. Lego® and other construction sets. Access to the hall for a short PE session

Teaching the lessons

Lesson 1

Key questions

Is this higher or lower?

Which is beside, behind, in front?

Vocabulary

Position, beside, behind, in front of, over, under, on top of, beneath, above, below, on, in, next to

Introduction | 10min |

▦ Invite a child to come to the front and play 'Miss Muffet' by sitting on a chair or stool and holding the bowl and spoon. Ask the children to chant the nursery rhyme and dangle the toy spider beside her. Then tell the children that the spider is going to sit somewhere else next time. Allow them to say the rhyme again (with another child playing the part) and this time the children should chant 'sat down behind her'. Repeat the rhyme again and again putting the spider in different places so that the children use a range of position words.

Activities | 30min |

▦ Hide six small objects around the room. Later tell the children what they are and allow them to see if they can spot them. Then call the children together and ask, for each object in turn, 'Where can it be found?' Retrieve the items one at a time as the children confirm and repeat the positions of the objects.

👤 Ask the children to complete **Copymaster 38**.

Closing the lesson | 15min |

▦ Allow a group of children to place small objects in various places around the room and announce the position of the object as they do so.

Assessment

Child performance	Teacher action
Cannot use a variety of appropriate words and terms to describe position	Give the children more practical sessions while giving a commentary and using position words. Then repeat the activities in this lesson
Lacks confidence in using some position words	Give the children a chance to do these activities again
Can use position words accurately and confidently	Move on to the next lesson

Lesson 2 ②

Key questions

Is this a left or right shoe?

Can you show me your right thumb?

Can you point to the right side of the board?

Vocabulary

Left, right, in the middle, on the left, on the right

Introduction   `15min`

Stick a large pair of hand-prints and footprints up on the board, each hand and foot labelled 'left' and 'right'. Ask the children to stand looking at the board. Invent a simple dance routine for the children to follow, such as left foot stamp, left foot stamp, right foot stamp, right foot stamp, left hand up, right hand up – and then repeat.

Try it out, calling 'left foot', 'left foot' and so on, in time to the actions. Ask the children to join in the actions and calling out. With some practice this could make a contribution to an assembly.

Activities   `35min`

Point out to the children the items on display and talk through the ideas about left and right, using their own clothing as well as that on display.

Ask each child to complete **Copymaster 39**.

Allow the children to work together tracing routes through the maze on **Copymaster 40**.

Closing the lesson   `5min`

Call out the left and right parts of things in the classroom, and ask the children to point to them. Thus, for example you could say, 'right hand door', 'the bookshelf on the left…'.

Assessment

Child performance	Teacher action
Cannot distinguish left and right	Give the children copious supervised practical experience involving left and right
Works with left and right but lacks confidence	Revise this lesson's activities and revisit it when doing PE work

Knows about left and right	Move on to the next lesson

Lesson 3

Key questions

Can you show me a turn all the way around?

Can you show me a turn halfway around?

Vocabulary

Turn, turning, halfway, a quarter of the way, around

Introduction   `10min`

Set out an array of things where turning is involved in their use. The display could involve, for example, a book, a child's spinning top, a pair of pliers, a rotary egg whisk, a plastic bottle with top, a pair of scissors, a toy car, a toy wheelbarrow. Show the children how these things turn and tell them that when we talk about turning, we mean a movement that is a complete rotation (getting back to the position at the start) or only part of this rotation.

Activities   `45min`

Invite the children, in their groups, to make a moving model using Lego® or other construction sets. The whole model should turn (as in a roundabout) or parts of it can turn (for example, wheels and cogs)

Take the children into the hall for a short PE session. Ask them to make turning movements in response to music. At first they can turn their whole body. Then they can follow the lead of another child in turning and changing direction. Then they can work 'on the spot' by turning only parts of the body.

Closing the lesson   `5min`

Allow the children to look at the models made in group work and examine where they are turning.

Assessment

Child performance	Teacher action
Does not explore and discuss turning movements	Begin work on this theme again
Needs more work on turning movements	Repeat some activities, particularly those in the previous lesson
Can explore and discuss turning movements	The learning targets for this theme have been met

HOMEWORK

Allow the children to take home copies of Copymaster 40 so that they can trace and discuss their routes.

THEME 15

Describing position and direction

Learning targets

The children should be able to:

1 ➻➔ Describe the position of given objects and some particular movements
2 ➻➔ Produce examples of repeat patterns
3 ➻➔ Give instructions to establish positions and directions

Before you start

Subject knowledge

As the children progress in their understanding and appropriate use of descriptive words and phrases related to position they should be encouraged to develop precision in their work. In this theme there are a variety of experiences that support the refinement of description. There are also links here with algebra in that consistent description that permits a sequence (in this case of movements) to be enacted by others is one of its major ideas. The work the children do here will act as a platform for later work on, for example, reading maps and producing logical sequences in all aspects of mathematics.

Previous knowledge required

Some vocabulary of position, some experience of work on turning

Resources needed for Lesson 1

A clockwork toy or a remote-controlled car, a ramp and an arch made out of construction blocks. Suitable video footage giving opportunities to describe movement and position. Access to the hall for a short PE lesson

Resources needed for Lesson 2

Instructions for pattern-making on the board. Copymaster 41. Squared paper (General Copymaster C)

Resources needed for Lesson 3

Paper, felt-tipped pens and sticky shapes.

Homework: Copymaster 42

Teaching the lessons

Lesson 1 ①

Key questions

Where is the (name of person, animal or object) now?

Can you describe how the (name of person, animal or object) is moving?

Vocabulary

forward, backwards, up, down (and words introduced in earlier themes, including beside, behind, in front of, over, under, on top of, beneath, above, below, on, in, next to, left, right, in the middle, on the left, on the right, turn, turning, halfway, a quarter of the way, around)

Introduction [10min]

▦ Using a clockwork toy or a remote-controlled car, a ramp and an arch made out of construction blocks, set the toy going and ask the class about its position and movements. For example it can be made to go under the arch, down the ramp, forwards, backwards, turn around and so on

Activities [45min]

▦ Show the children some suitable video footage giving opportunities to describe movement and position of objects, people, or animals (such as news items about traffic or shopping and animal wildlife programmes).

▦ Take the children into the hall for a short PE lesson. Give each child a bean bag and ask them to follow directions involving position and direction words, placing the beanbag in front of them, beneath them, to the right and so on, as indicated in the Vocabulary section opposite.

Closing the lesson [5min]

▦ Back in class ask a child to place a beanbag in different locations and the class can say where it is in relation to the child.

Assessment

Child performance	Teacher action
Finds it difficult to describe position and movements	Consider repeating some of the work from the previous theme before returning to this theme

Needs more practice with position and movement

Has a good understanding of position and movement and an extensive vocabulary

Repeat some of the things the children have done in this lesson

Move on to the next lesson

Lesson 2 ②

Key questions

What comes next?

In what position is the next shape?

Can you continue the pattern?

Vocabulary

All the vocabulary the children have met so far, and any additional words that are in everyday vocabulary. These words include those in the vocabulary list for Lesson 1: forward, backwards, up, down, beside, behind, in front of, over, under, on top of beneath, above, below, on, in, next to, left, right, in the middle, on the left, on the right, turn, turning, halfway, a quarter of the way, around

Introduction ⟨10 min⟩

▓ Show the children a pattern drawn on the board. Begin with a simple one as shown here:

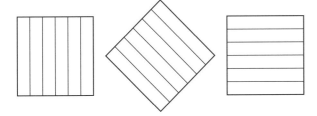

The pattern here is moving from left to right and the blob moves up and down. Try a more complex pattern which involves a shape turning as well as moving along. Here is an example:

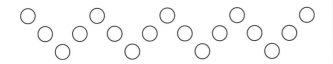

Activities ⟨30 min⟩

▓ Ask the children to begin a pattern on squared paper, following the directions you give them on the board. On the board draw a pattern of squares thus:

The row should match the number of squares on the Copymaster. Ask the children to colour the top right hand corner of the first square. Colour this one on the board. Then ask them to colour the bottom right hand corner in the next square. Colour this on the board. Then give similar instructions for the next two

squares, colouring the bottom left and top left corners respectively. For the next square return to the top right hand corner.

 Now ask the children to continue the pattern on the squared paper for several rows of squares. They can then invent a pattern for themselves and work it through for several rows.

 Ask the children to complete **Copymaster 41**.

Closing the lesson ⟨10 min⟩

▓ Make up a simple sequence of hand and arm actions. Give the children instructions so that they can follow it through. Then ask a child to be the 'caller' and describe the sequence as the children are doing it.

Assessment

Child performance	Teacher action
Finds it hard to produce examples of repeat patterns	Give the children copious opportunities to copy and invent patterns
Needs more chances to follow directions and make repeat patterns	Repeat some of the activities in this and related lessons
Can make repeat patterns	Move on to the next lesson

Lesson 3 ③

Key questions

What is your next position going to be?

How are you going to move to there?

What is your position in relation to (name of classmate)?

Vocabulary

The children will be demonstrating the breadth of their vocabulary in this lesson, and therefore should be using many of the following: forward, backwards, up, down, beside, behind, in front of, over, under, on top of, beneath, above, below, on, in, next to, left, right, in the middle, on the left, on the right, turn, turning, halfway, a quarter of the way, around

Introduction ⟨10 min⟩

▓ Act out a nursery rhyme with some of the children while the others look on. For example, if the rhyme is Jack and Jill, give the children position and direction instructions, thus: 'Jack, please stand beside Jill holding the bucket in the middle, between you. The hill is to your right. Walk forwards…' and so on.

Activities ⟨30 min⟩

 Invite each group of children to work on a different nursery rhyme and agree the instructions for carrying it out. Each group can enact it, with one person giving all the directions. All the groups can watch one another's work.

 Ask the children to use paper, felt-tipped pens, sticky shapes and other resources to make a greetings card. They can then agree detailed specific instructions for making it. These can be written down or recorded on tape.

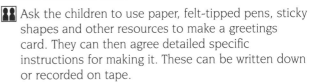

Closing the lesson

| 10 min |

Use a giant outline of a child. Ask individual children to place flashcards showing position words in appropriate positions such as the examples in the illustrations on the right.

Assessment

Child performance	Teacher action
Cannot give instructions to establish positions and directions	Allow the children to work on this vocabulary in repeated short sessions
Can give some directions	Give the children more opportunities to direct classmates in activities
Can use position and direction vocabulary well	The learning targets for this theme have been met

HOMEWORK

Invite the children to draw a comic story on **Copymaster 42** with captions that use direction and position words.

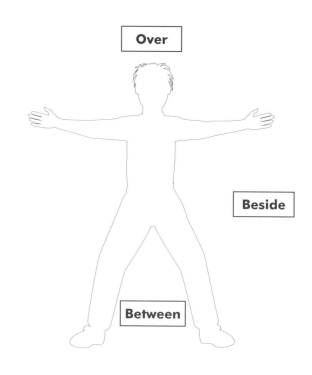

Angles

Learning targets

The children should be able to:

1 ➡→ Use the term angle

2 ➡→ Find right angles

3 ➡→ Select angles that are more or less than a right angle

Before you start

Subject knowledge

In this theme the concern is mainly with static angles. The corners of objects will be very familiar to the children and they will be able to provide many examples. The angle that corners make is related to their function. Commonly corners are right angles, for example, tables, books, door-frames and doors, the corners in rooms and so on. Right angles are important to us just as they have been in many civilisations. The Ancient Egyptians needed, for example, to establish right angles for the bases of the Pyramids. We understand that they did this by using rope knotted at regular intervals, and pegs, and using the knowledge that a triangle with the dimension five knots by four knots by three knots is a right angled triangle. A simple check using Pythagoras' theorem confirms this fact: five squared does equal four squared plus three squared. Along with an understanding of the right angle the children will come to understand what is meant by a straight angle and the relationships between the right angle, the straight angle and one complete rotation.

Previous knowledge required

Positional language

Resources needed for Lesson 1

Display of 3-D and 2-D shapes, dolls' house, toy wheelbarrow, Copymaster 43, pieces of stiff card, and resources for printing (that is foam pads soaked in thick poster paint set down in plastic trays like those in which supermarket meat, fish and cakes are sold), paper

Resources needed for Lesson 2

Rough paper, card templates of 2-D shapes (including triangles, quadrilaterals – with squares and rectangles among them – pentagons, hexagons, circles) enough for each work group to have at least two different examples of each shape. Copymaster 44

Resources needed for Lesson 3

Card templates of 2-D shapes, geostrips, Copymasters 45 and 46

Teaching the lessons

Lesson 1 ①

Key questions

What do we call this?

Can you point to an angle here?

Vocabulary

Angle, turn, bend

Introduction 5min

▦ Point to the corner of the board, the corner of a book and the corners of a large set square, and tell the children that we can measure corners like this using a measurement called an angle. The angles the children are looking at here are those formed where two lines (in these cases the edges of the objects) meet. Point out the display and tell the children that in this lesson they will be looking for angles. Show the children that we indicate an angle on our work using this mark:

Activities 40min

👥 Using items from the display, which they can borrow and put back one at a time, the children should talk about the angles they can find. Walk around the groups to challenge them to find more angles.

👥 Invite the children to see how many angles they can find on **Copymaster 43** and mark them in with an angle mark. While they are doing this, a group at a time can attempt the next activity.

👥 Ask the children to dip card edges into paint pads and then print with these, creating angles as shown here. This work will make a backdrop to subsequent work on angle.

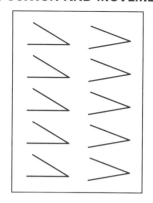
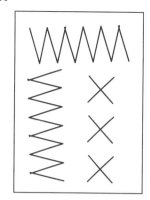

Closing the lesson

[5 min]

Invite a child to pick up things around the room and show the rest of the class where there is an angle.

Assessment

Child performance	Teacher action
Cannot use the term angle	Give the children individual attention and explain the facts given in the introduction to the lesson again. Then repeat the activities of the lesson
Uses the term angle but cannot identify angles in some circumstances	Give the children more opportunities to identify where there are angles
Confident in identifying and naming angles	Move on to the next lesson

Lesson 2 (2)

Key questions

Can you point to a right angle?

Can you name this angle?

How many right angles has this shape?

Vocabulary

angle, right angle, measure

Introduction

[10 min]

Remind the children of their work on angle as a measurement, in the previous lesson. Tell them that mathematicians give names to different sizes of angle, and one of these is called a right angle. Show the children the corner of the room at floor and ceiling level and other items which have exact right angles. Draw a right angle on the board and put in the right angle sign on it, as shown here:

Activities

[40 min]

Show the children how to make their own right angle measurer from rough paper as shown here:

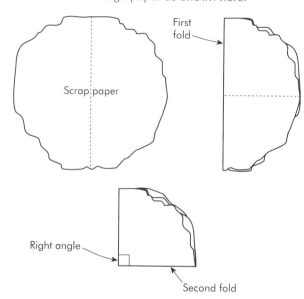

Ask the children to test some angles they can find around the room and identify some right angles. Give the children a few minutes to do this and then bring the class together, so that each child can name one right angle they found.

Ask the children to look carefully at the card templates of 2-D shapes, and sort out those that have right angles. Check the groups' decisions in a whole class discussion

Ask the children to complete **Copymaster 44**, identifying the right angles there.

Closing the lesson

[5 min]

Show the children some sample right angles in objects, and tell them that angle is a measure and the measure is made in degrees. A right angle is said to measure 90 degrees. The symbol for degrees is °.

Assessment

Child performance	Teacher action
Cannot find right angles	Give the children individual help in looking at right angles and naming them
Finds some right angles	Allow more time for the child to find right angles, in group, pair and individual settings
Has a clear understanding of what a right angle is and finds many examples	Move on to the next lesson

Lesson 3 (3)

Key questions

Can you see an angle here?

Is this angle a right angle?

Is it more than or less than a right angle?

46

Vocabulary

Angle, measure, right angle, more than, less than

Introduction 10 min

 Show the children two geostrips or other apparatus, fixed together to make a right angle. Ask them what this kind of angle is called. Then show them another pair of strips made into an angle smaller than a right angle, and yet another made into an angle greater than a right angle. Compare them all so that the children can see the difference.

Activities 40 min

Before the lesson set up 12 geostrip angles around the room. They can be clipped to backing board so that the angles between them cannot be tampered with. Number them from 1 to 12. Invite the children to go around and look (but not touch), and draw the angles on **Copymaster 45**, naming them 'right angle', 'less than' or 'more than'.

Ask the children to look carefully at each of the card templates of 2-D shapes and work out whether the angles are less then, or more than right angles, or exact right angles in each.

Ask the children to use what they know in working with the angles on **Copymaster 46**.

Closing the lesson 5 min

Look at an example of each of the 2-D shapes the groups worked with in turn, and allow the children to comment on the angles in the shape.

Assessment

Child performance	Teacher action
Cannot sort angles and say they are more or less than a right angle	Give the children individual help with angle, before repeating work in this theme
Has difficulty identifying some angles	Give more supervised practice at angle ident-ification
Can sort angles with alacrity	The learning targets for this theme have been met

HOMEWORK

Invite the children to take home their right angle measurer and draw four things in each of the rooms in their house, that demonstrate right angles.

THEME 17

Angle, movement and direction

Learning targets

The children should be able to:

1 ➡➡ Identify clockwise or anti-clockwise in whole turns
2 ➡➡ Make and describe simple patterns of movement using turns and simple fractions of a turn
3 ➡➡ Use rulers to draw straight lines

Before you start

Subject knowledge

In this theme we are mainly concerned with the dynamic characteristics of angle. Using their own movements the children should be able to see that, whilst we can hold a position, we are essentially in motion and we can make a range of angles and rotations with our bodies. To describe these it is necessary not only to use positional and directional vocabulary but also to apply other mathematics such as the use of simple fractions. These fractions of a turn, such as a half and a quarter can be related to a wide range of experiences that the children will already have had. For example, telling the time with halves and quarters, cutting fruit into whole, half and quarter pieces, and the use of repeat patterns in art. Finally in order to consider that a line might rotate (like the hand on a clock) it is necessary for the children to appreciate how to draw straight lines using a ruler and then to be able to connect points using straight lines. This is not easy to do and much practice needs to be offered, including not only paper and pencil exercises, but also on a larger scale, for example across the playground.

Previous knowledge required

Vocabulary of movement and position, static angle (as in right angle at the corner of a room)

Resources needed for Lesson 1

Clock face with hands that can be turned. Large screw top jar with lid. Display of items where turn is involved in their use, including, for example, a rotary can opener, a rotary egg whisk, a garlic press, plastic screw top jars and bottles, a padlock and key. Copymasters 47 and 48

Resources needed for Lesson 2

Access to the hall for a PE lesson. Card templates of 2-D shapes. Card, scissors and paper fasteners. Copymaster 49. Floor robot

Resources needed for Lesson 3

Rulers, chalk, board ruler, metre sticks. A large dot-to-dot puzzle. Copymaster 50

Teaching the lessons

Lesson 1 ①

Key questions

Which way does this turn?

Can you turn it halfway around?

How far around have I turned?

Vocabulary

Turn, around, clockwise, anti-clockwise, half turn, quarter turn, angle, right angle

Introduction ⏱10min

▦ Show the children the clock face. Wind the hands around on the face and ask the children to trace in the air the direction of the turn. Tell the children that this direction of turn is called clockwise, and turning the other way round is called anti-clockwise. Now show the children the large screw top jar with lid, and invite a child to unscrew the lid while the class looks on. Ask the children about the direction of turn. Then put the lid back on, showing the children the direction of turn this time.

Activities ⏱35min

⚫⚫ Ask a group to do this activity while the rest of the class do the other activities, and then they can swop about. They should investigate the items on display, one at a time, and find out the direction(s) of turn in each case. They can record their findings, using their own methods, ready for the class plenary session.

👥 Using a set of flashcards made up from **Copymaster 47** each pair of children should answer the challenges, saying whether the turning action is clockwise or anti-clockwise.

👤 Invite the children to complete **Copymaster 48** and then discuss their work.

Closing the lesson ⏱10min

▦ Ask each group to choose a different object from the display and say in which way it, or part of it, is turned when using it.

Assessment

Child performance	Teacher action
Cannot identify clockwise and anti-clockwise in whole turns	Introduce the topic of turn again to the children
Investigates turns but not yet confident in this work	Give more practice including activities like those in this lesson
Accurately identifies direction of turn	Move on to the next lesson

Lesson 2 ②

Key questions

Can you turn all the way/halfway/a quarter of the way around?

What part of a turn is this?

Vocabulary

Turn, whole, halfway, a quarter of the way, revolve, revolution, right, left

Introduction ⎢5min⎢

 Stand a child volunteer in front of the class, and move the child physically right around to show a complete turn, and then halfway around, and then a quarter of the way around, pointing out what is happening as you do so.

Activities ⎢40min⎢

 During a PE lesson, give the children instructions that involve turning movements. Then invite them to work with a partner, where one child issues turning instructions and the other follows them.

Following the instructions on **Copymaster 49** ask the children to make a picture or pattern involving turning a shape. (The children can cut their own shape from card or use ready cut shapes).

Allow children to issue directions to a child so that he or she can operate the controls for a floor robot. The whole class can stand around the 'arena' and watch.

Closing the lesson ⎢5min⎢

Show the class some of the work on pattern making done during the lesson.

Assessment

Child performance	Teacher action
Cannot make and describe simple patterns of movement using turns and simple fractions of a turn	During PE and games lessons give the children the chance to practice following instructions, and issuing directions to classmates
Makes turns but lacks confidence in description	Allow the children to commentate on others' movements in a PE lesson
Can make and describe patterns of turn	Move on to the next lesson

Lesson 3 ③

Key questions

Are you holding the ruler still?

Have you drawn a straight line here?

Vocabulary

Straight line

Introduction ⎢10min⎢

 Point out to the children that it is quite difficult to draw a straight line, but as mathematicians we need to learn to do so. Demonstrate how the ruler needs to be held steady, and how the pencil needs holding. Draw several lines while the children look on. Then let some of the children have a go.

Activities ⎢35min⎢

Allow the children a chance to practice drawing lines on rough paper.

 Take the children onto the playground, where, using board rulers or metre sticks and chalk they can draw some straight lines.

Ask the children to complete **Copymaster 50** using straight lines.

Closing the lesson ⎢10min⎢

 Show the children a large sheet of paper with a dot to dot picture on it. Invite individuals to join up the dots with straight lines. Display the finished picture.

Assessment

Child performance	Teacher action
Cannot use a ruler to draw straight lines	Give the children many opportunities to practise drawing lines with a ruler
Not yet adept at drawing straight lines	Give the children many opportunities to practise drawing lines with a ruler
Can draw straight lines with a ruler	The learning targets for this theme have been met

HOMEWORK

Ask the children to draw a maze or track involving quarter, half and whole turns on paper and then write or draw instructions about how to traverse it. Thus the pictures showing what to do could be like this:

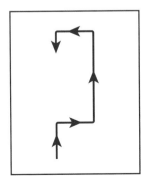

Quarter turns
Forward 1 unit
Turn right
Forward 1 unit
Turn left
Forward 2 units
Turn left
Forward 1 unit
Turn left

Investigations

- Using programmable robots the children can programme movements in sequence.
- Make up a sequence of movements in PE using turns and part turns. Individual children can do them, with a commentary, in front of the class.
- Create a collaborative treasure hunt, with direction clues.
- Make a collection of jigsaw puzzles. Talk about why some are more difficult to do than others.

- Make a collection of pictures showing reflection or rotation. These could be from magazines or comics. Collect repeat patterns, like braid or wallpaper borders.
- Experiment with lines on paper to make curves, corners, thick and thin lines.
- Make patterns using different 2-D shapes. Try making reflections of these patterns. Look for reflections in paper goods like serviettes and doilies.

Assessment

- Make a variety of cut and torn paper shapes and display these. Talk about which way up, and where they should go on the display. Turn the shapes and talk about the effects of turning.

- Draw everyday things that are turned when used.
- Follow directions involving instructions that use left and right; forwards and backwards; and clockwise and anti-clockwise.

MEASURES AND DATA

Measuring is an age-old human activity. After counting, measuring is probably the next mathematical activity that people developed. Measurement continues to be of central importance to us and the search for more and more accurate measurements is a touchstone for any exploration of the history of ideas. Early measures were concerned, primarily, with the tangible. Weights, lengths and volumes are all important in this respect as they are involved in the trading of goods. From early times people used comparisons to gauge these sorts of dimensions. The units were often non-standard and involved dimensions of the human body. We still use such approaches today. For example, in judging dimensions for curtains, or turning up hems of skirts or trousers; or on the market stall where lengths of cloth are measured from nose tip to arm's length. So in giving our children experience in making comparisons using themselves or other non-standard measures we are working with the important principles of measurement.

As people needed to measure more consistently the need for standard measures came to be recognised. A range of 'standards' was established at different times and places. For example, the cubit was an early measure. It is the distance from the point of the elbow to the tip of the middle finger. Fractions of a cubit were based on thumb lengths with eighteen thumbs being seen as one cubit. However, cubits were not convenient for measuring distances, so the 'foot' became popular. Greek and Roman 'feet' were different. The greeks used a foot of about 11.69 inches and that of the Romans was about 11.61 inches. In medieval England, a foot of 12.45 inches was commonly used. As trade became more widespread and new technologies meant that people could construct more complex tools and buildings, it was necessary to standardise such measurements and in this country we settled on a measure of length where 12 inches equalled one foot and 3 feet equalled one yard. This of course does not guarantee standards unless we have something consistent against which to calibrate our rulers or tapes. For this purpose a standard yard was cast, and this was used to establish a precise comparison. In similar fashion, over time, standard measures were created for all types of measurement. Today we use our knowledge of atoms and electrons to establish standards and we have moved from imperial standards to metric ones. But all of the reasons for standard measures are the same as they always were: consistency, accuracy and fairness. The reason we have pointed up some aspects of the development of standard measures is that it is possible to see the evolution of thinking about measurement. It is our experience that taking children through a similar evolutionary track helps them to understand the principles, not just memorise the units. So in the early years it is vital that children engage in much practical measuring work and are allowed to make extensive use of non-standard measures. This will allow them to develop an understanding of why we need standard measures, the importance of the appropriateness of units, the need for accuracy, and the value of approximation and estimation.

Introducing length

Learning targets

The children should be able to:

1 ➤➤ Use the vocabulary of length

2 ➤➤ Make comparisons of length

3 ➤➤ Use non-standard measures of length

Before you start

Subject knowledge

This theme begins the measures section of the book for we view length as being the concept that is most readily accessible to children. They start by working with some vocabulary and have opportunities to make comparisons. Note that the words included have to do with overall size, in addition to length. This theme then sets the scene for an introduction to area. There is an enormous vocabulary to be addressed here, so the basic lesson structure may need to be repeated several times, for all children, to help them to master the language of length. Non-standard measures are thought to have been the kinds of rough approximations made by humans in prehistoric times. They lie at the root of many of the standard measures in use today.

Previous knowledge required

Everyday experience of the lengths of things

Resources needed for Lesson 1

Flashcards showing size words including the following: long, longer, longest; short, shorter, shortest; tall, taller, tallest; wide, wider, widest; big, bigger, biggest; large, larger, largest; small, smaller, smallest; little, littler, littlest; broad, broader, broadest; narrow, narrower, narrowest; thin, thinner, thinnest; fat, fatter, fattest; and any others that are in local use. A box of assorted everyday items that will be a stimulus for discussion. It may include some items from the kitchen including spoons; from the bathroom such as flannels and bath brush; books and toys of a range of sizes; items from the natural world, including sticks, cones, shells. Copymasters 51 and 52

Resources needed for Lesson 2

A display of items that can be set in order of size. These can include very small things like fruit pips, to very long things like a skipping rope. Copymaster 53. A box of similar items of different dimensions for each workgroup. For example the boxes could contain construction blocks, toys with wheels, finger and glove puppets, play dough cakes and biscuits. Rectangular card offcuts of varying lengths and widths

Resources needed for Lesson 3

Display chart of some non-standard measures, as shown below. Copymaster 54. A box of items that can be used as arbitrary measuring tools, including sticks, blocks, pasta pieces like macaroni, pencils. Copymaster 55

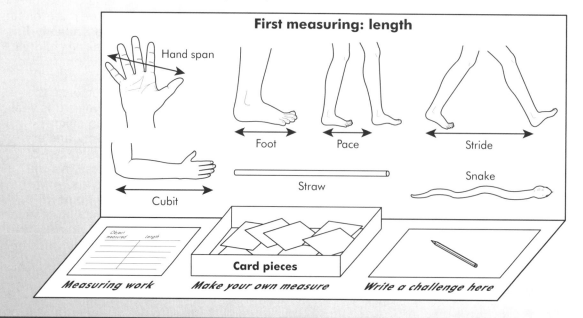

First measuring: length

Hand span

Foot

Pace

Stride

Cubit

Straw

Snake

Object measured / length

Card pieces

Measuring work

Make your own measure

Write a challenge here

Teaching the lessons

Lesson 1

Key questions

Which is the longer/taller/bigger/smaller/broader/thinner of these?

Which is the longest/tallest/biggest/smallest/broadest/thinnest?

Look at these two things. What can you tell me about their sizes?

Vocabulary

long, longer, longest; short, shorter, shortest

tall, taller, tallest; wide, wider, widest

big, bigger, biggest; large, larger, largest

small, smaller, smallest; little, littler, littlest

broad, broader, broadest; narrow, narrower, narrowest

thin, thinner, thinnest; fat, fatter, fattest

and any other size words that are in local use.

Introduction `10min`

 Ask two children to stand in front of the class, and draw comparisons between them. Note that we say taller, shorter, smaller when making comparisons of two people or things. Try the activity again with two different children, and ask the children to supply the comparison words.

Now repeat the activity with three children, using small-smaller-smallest, tall-taller-tallest and similar vocabulary.

Activities `45min`

 Give each group a set of small flashcards made up from **Copymaster 51**. Ask them to lay out the array of words so that all the children in the group can see them. Using a large matching set of flashcards, hold up each in turn and say it aloud. The children should take it in turns to find the matching card in their set, and put it on one side. Add other flashcards to the set to reflect the words the children actually use.

Using the flashcards used in the previous activity if necessary, the children should complete **Copymaster 52**.

Take a selection of items that offer opportunities for size comparisons, from a box of assorted everyday items. Discuss the words that can be used to compare these. Invite several children in turn, to make their own selection from the box and discuss their comparisons in front of the class.

Closing the lesson `5min`

Hold up flashcards from the classroom set at random, and ask the children to call out what they say.

Assessment

Child performance	Teacher action
Cannot use the vocabulary of size	Begin by allowing the children to handle and talk about objects of different sizes. Then repeat the activities of this lesson, over several sessions if necessary
Uses some size vocabulary	Check the vocabulary that the children are unfamiliar with and give specific practice, repeating activities like those in this lesson
Confidently talks about and reads a wide range of size words	Move on to the next lesson

Lesson 2

Key questions

Can you put these in size order, starting with the shortest?

Which comes next in order of length/height...?

Vocabulary

Words like those introduced in lesson 1, namely:

long, longer, longest; short, shorter, shortest

tall, taller, tallest; wide, wider, widest

big, bigger, biggest; large, larger, largest

small, smaller, smallest; little, littler, littlest

broad, broader, broadest; narrow, narrower, narrowest

thin, thinner, thinnest; fat, fatter, fattest

Introduction `10min`

 Before the lesson set up a small display, with some items on it that can be placed in order of size. Examples could include very small things like fruit pips and very long things like skipping ropes. Show the children how we can decide on the kinds of comparisons to make and set the things out in order. The display can then be left up during the lesson and beyond, and be added to with samples of the children's work.

Activities `40min`

Invite each group to use a box of items (for example, construction blocks, toys with wheels, finger and glove puppets, play dough cakes and biscuits) and set them out in different rankings according to dimensions. The children can record these sorts with the key words on large sheets of paper. Their record may look like the diagram on page 54.

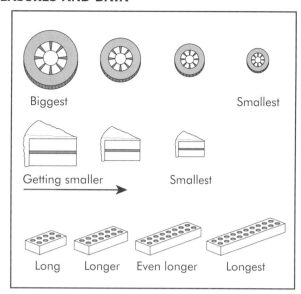

Biggest · Smallest

Getting smaller → Smallest

Long · Longer · Even longer · Longest

👤 Ask the children to order the pictures on **Copymaster 53**.

Closing the lesson　🔲 5min

▨ Using card off-cuts, show the children how these can be ordered, using a range of vocabulary including words like wider and broader, which may be less familiar to the children.

Assessment

Child performance	Teacher action
Finds it difficult to make comparisons of length	Return to the remediation suggestions for Lesson 1 and then repeat that lesson before trying Lesson 2 again
Can compare lengths but needs more practice	Give the children plenty of opportunities to make length comparisons, over several sessions
Confident and articulate about length comparisons	Move on to the next lesson

Lesson 3　③

Key questions

How many hand spans across the desk?

How many paces is it across the room?

Is the hall more than 25 strides long?

How many thumbs do you think would fit the length of your reading book?

Vocabulary

Hand span, cubit, foot, pace, stride, thumb

Introduction　🔲 10min

▨ Show the children the display chart of non-standard measures, and talk through what they are called. Show the children exactly how to measure, using these, pointing out how to achieve an accurate measure (for example, by placing thumb and

fingertips touching when working with hand spans, and making steps as close to the same size as possible when using paces).

Activities　🔲 40min

👥 Write up on the board about six measuring tasks that the children can do in pairs around the room. Choose tasks where they can do them without getting in one another's way, and ask some children to start at number 1, some 2 and so on. Draw a picture beside each challenge to show what measure the children should use. Here are some examples.

Across a table

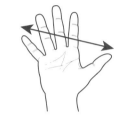

Along a bookshelf

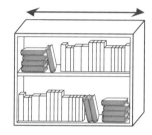
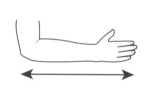

Across the room

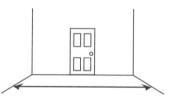
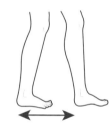

👤 Ask the children to try the measuring challenges on

👥 **Copymaster 54**. This task can be done individually or in pairs, but the children should each make their own record.

👤 Write up on the board another set of measuring challenges that the children can do, using either an arbitrary measure from the box of items that can be used as arbitrary measuring tools, including sticks, blocks, pasta pieces like macaroni, pencils or a measure of their choice that they can make (or can be made up ahead of the lesson) from **Copymaster 55**.

Closing the lesson　🔲 10min

▨ Invite individual children to talk about the measuring they have done, using 'body parts' or arbitrary measures. Point out that we choose a unit of measurement according to the task. Thus we would not measure the hall using pencils, or a book using a skipping rope.

Assessment

Child performance	Teacher action
Cannot use non-standard measures of length	Give the child opportunities, over several sessions, to use each of a range of non-standard measures in turn. Then repeat this lesson
Uses some measures but needs more experience of the range of measures	Repeat a list of measuring exercises, using a range of different measures, over several sessions
Can use a wide range of non-standard measures	Check that the children have used the full range of non-standard units, before moving on to another theme

HOMEWORK

Allow the children to draw a 'fun to measure' tool of their own (shaped like a creature of their choice). They can then use this to make measurements around their home. Alternatively ask the children to create a small note-book entitled 'Non-standard measure work book'. On each page they should make four different measurements using, for example, hand spans on one page, a pencil on the next and so on.

Introducing mass

Learning targets

The children should be able to:

1 ➡ Talk about mass

2 ➡ Compare masses

3 ➡ Use non-standard measures of mass

Before you start

Subject knowledge

Mass and weight are not the same thing. Weight varies, depending on the force of gravity. However, now is not the time to embroil the children in this distinction. We believe that we should talk about 'weight' vocabulary, as this is so familiar to the children. The definitions and distinctions can come later. Comparing (that is balancing one object against another) and the use of non-standard measures are vital first steps. Ordering in respect of heavier and lighter are also key ideas and form the basis of some crucial experiences.

Previous knowledge required

'Play' experience of weighing things

Resources needed for Lesson 1

Classroom balance and bathroom scales Flashcards with the following words on them: light, lighter, lightest; heavy, heavier, heaviest. For each work group, a box of items that can easily be held in the hand. These could include,

for example, pebbles, foam sponge, cotton wool balls, table tennis ball, beanbag, small basket or box. The contents of the box can be replicated for each work group, but this is not essential; the boxes can carry different items so long as there is a variety of items of different masses in each

Resources needed for Lesson 2

Copymaster 56. A display of items, the masses of which can be compared. (If this lesson is being done close to Lesson 1, the items here should differ from those used in Lesson 1.) Here are some examples: plastic cups, wooden blocks, boxes, sticks, cones, bags containing rice, and pasta, small tins of foodstuffs.

Resources needed for Lesson 3

Classroom balances, enough for at least one per work group, but one per pair of children would be better. Things that can be weighed and items that can be used as 'units' for weighing such as beads and pasta shapes. They can be set out as shown below. Copymaster 57.

Homework: Copymaster 58

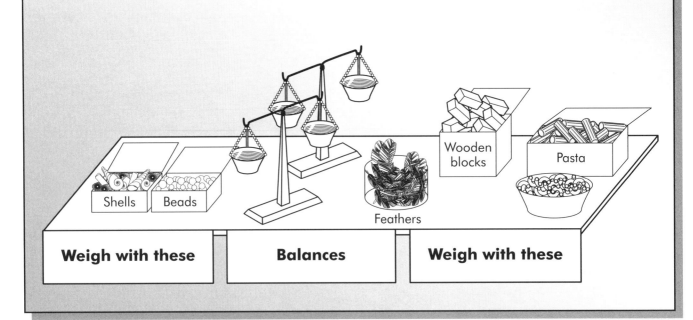

Shells | Beads

Wooden blocks

Pasta

Feathers

Weigh with these | **Balances** | **Weigh with these**

Teaching the lessons

Lesson 1

Key questions

What do we do when we weigh things

Vocabulary

Balance, scales, weigh, light, lighter, lightest; heavy, heavier, heaviest

Introduction | 10 min

Discuss with the children the idea that we weigh things. Take up some small items that can be held in the hand and make some judgements about which is heavier and lighter. Pass them around so that some of the children can make judgements too.

Activities | 30 min

Using classroom flashcards with the following words on them: light, lighter, lightest; heavy, heavier, heaviest, take one at a time, hold it up in front of the children and read it aloud before they read it back to you. Point out the endings to the words to assist the children in spelling them.

Give each work group a box of items that can easily be held in the hand. These could include, for example, pebbles, foam sponge, cotton wool balls, a table tennis ball, beanbag, small basket or box. Ask the children to compare the items by taking up two at a time, one in each hand. They can all try the comparisons, and record the items putting them in order of mass. This can either be done as a group exercise, with the children working towards agreement on the comparisons, or each child can make their own record.

Closing the lesson | 10 min

Talk to the children about the problems of making comparisons by holding things, or picking them up. Point out that we use a range of tools to weigh things. Show the children the classroom balance and bathroom scales, indicating that we use different weighing tools for different kinds of jobs.

Assessment

Child performance	Teacher action
Cannot talk about why we weigh things and what we do to weigh them	Give the children individual attention to discuss their own experiences about weighing, before moving on to the idea of comparison and repeating this lesson
Makes comparisons about weight and uses some vocabulary	Give the children more practice in using the vocabulary of weighing
Confident and articulate about weighing	Move on to the next lesson

Lesson 2

Key questions

Which is heavier?

Which of these is heaviest?

Which is lighter?

Which of these is lightest?

Vocabulary

Balance, scales, weigh, light, lighter, lightest; heavy, heavier, heaviest

Introduction | 5 min

Remind the children of the vocabulary of comparing mass, and that we say lighter, heavier when comparing two things but lightest and heaviest when comparing three or more things.

Activities | 35 min

Ask the children to use their judgement in completing **Copymaster 56**.

Give each group a box of items, the masses of which can be compared. There should be at least three or four of each item. (If this lesson is being done close to Lesson 1, the items here should differ from those used in Lesson 1). Here are some examples: plastic cups, wooden blocks, boxes, sticks, cones, bags containing rice and pasta, and small tins of foodstuffs. The group should work together to establish the order they assign to each of the items of the same kind. Thus their results may look like this:

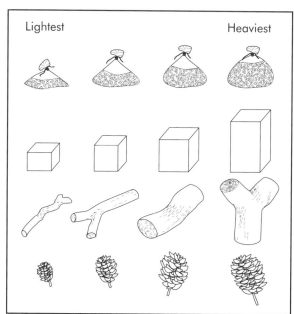

Allow the children the chance to go around the room and look at the rankings made by other groups.

Closing the lesson | 10 min

Play a 'heavier' and then a 'lighter' game, by calling out things like 'pencil' or 'feather' and asking children in quick-fire succession to name something heavier. A typical string may be: feather (heavier), paper clip (heavier), 2p coin (heavier), pen (heavier), tea cup (heavier), book…

Assessment

Child performance	Teacher action
Cannot compare masses	Give the children practical 'play' with a toy balance. Talk over what they are doing and what they expect to happen. Work on weighing vocabulary and then repeat this lesson
Needs more practice of these concepts	Give the children more practice in activities like those in this lesson and the one before it
Competent in working with concepts about mass	Move on to the next lesson

Lesson 3 ③

Key questions

Which is heavier? How can we tell this by looking at the balance?

Which is lighter?

What do you expect to happen, when the things are put in the balance pans?

How do you know that these things weigh the same?

How many fir cones/pencils/pasta shells will balance with the wood block/glove/eraser?

Vocabulary

Balance, scales, weigh, the same, light, lighter, lightest; heavy, heavier, heaviest

Introduction

15min

Set up one balance so that all the children can see it. Show the children how to use the balance properly, and how to interpret the movement of the pointer. Weigh two things, separately, using different arbitrary units, while the children look on. Then choose individual children to try some weighing, while the other children watch. Ask all the children about what is going on, giving them the chance to use the key vocabulary.

Activities

35min

If possible allow the children to work in pairs, on a set of challenges using a classroom balance. The challenges should be set out on the board, and will be determined by the items available in the classroom as 'units' for weighing. These could, for example, be Lego® pieces, conkers, or pasta shells. The challenges should still include things like 'Which is lighter?' but also include 'How many conkers balance with one Plasticine® blob?' 'How many pasta shells balance with two pencils?' Check that all the children in the class are getting the chance to do some weighing.

Ask the children to make a record of some of the weighing they have done on **Copymaster 57**.

Closing the lesson

5min

Rehearse again the key concepts when weighing by giving the children quick-fire questions like these:

When the pan goes down what does this tell us?

Which way will the pointer go when these are on the pan?

What does the pointer tell us?

How can I make these balance one another?

How can I find out which is the heaviest of these three things?

Assessment

Child performance	Teacher action
Cannot use a balance or non-standard measures of mass	Allow the children to explore the use of a 'play' balance, with adult super-vision and questioning. Then repeat some of the activities set out in this theme
Finds it difficult to carry through a range of weighing tasks	Give the children the opportunity to repeat work done in this lesson
Competent in doing weighing tasks	Move on to another theme

HOMEWORK

Give the children **Copymaster 58**, which comprises a number of challenges like those met in these lessons, which the children can work on at home.

Introducing capacity and volume

Learning targets

The children should be able to:

1 ➤➤ Explore containers by filling and emptying them
2 ➤➤ Compare capacity and volume of a range of containers
3 ➤➤ Use non-standard measures of capacity and volume

Before you start

Subject knowledge

There are two issues to consider when working with capacity and volume ideas. We all have problems with conservation of volume. For example, try estimating the capacity of an 8-inch (20cm) shallow sponge tin in terms of pints (litres) of water it will hold. The problem often seems to be that we equate height with volume. This problem is compounded if we move children to using a vertical scale to read off volume too soon. What we need to do is to give them lots of practical experiences in comparing capacities. The second issue is to do with the words and what they mean. Capacity is met more often in every day life but when, for example, we talk about a football ground being 'full to capacity', we are clearly not using the term in the same way as saying that a jug has a particular capacity. Volume too has a variety of uses. For example a central heating engineer would be interested in the volume of a room to determine radiator size whilst car manufacturers talk of the cubic capacity of their engines. We feel that in the early stages we should make more use of the term 'capacity' and not attempt to define the terms.

Previous knowledge required

Everyday experience with substances like sand and sugar, and liquids like water and milk

Resources needed for Lesson 1

Water trays or large bowls of water (enough for each work group to have one) and containers to fill, including the following for each work group: egg-cups, beakers, jugs, bowls, patty tins, shallow containers. Plastic aprons and sleeve protectors. Sand trays can be used also. Copymaster 59

Resources needed for Lesson 2

As in Lesson 1, water trays or large bowls of water (enough for each work group to have one) and containers to fill, including the following for each work group: egg-cups, beakers, jugs, bowls, patty tins, shallow containers. Plastic aprons and sleeve protectors. Sand trays can also be used. Copymaster 60

Resources needed for Lesson 3

As in Lesson 1, water trays or large bowls of water (enough for each work group to have one) and containers to fill, including the following for each work group: egg-cups, beakers, jugs, bowls, patty tins, shallow containers. Sand trays can also be used. Copymaster 61. Bring two or three large pans into school for the children to look at, or, if possible, invite a school cook to do so.

Homework: Copymaster 62

Teaching the lessons

Lesson 1 ①

Key questions

Can you fill this container?

Is this full yet?

Which of these containers is empty?

What shall we use to fill this cup?

Vocabulary

Fill, full, empty, pour, liquid, runny, container

Introduction 15min

▓ As this is an exploratory lesson it is important that the children spend as much time as possible gaining practical experience. Point out the safety and care rules about the use of water and sand, and emphasise that everyone should have turns at working with the water or sand. Talk about and demonstrate the words 'full' and 'empty'.

Recite rhymes and songs like 'Baa baa black sheep' (three bags full) and 'One, two, buckle my shoe' (my plate's empty) and 'I'm a little teapot' (pour me out) where there are references to the vocabulary the children will be using.

Activities 　　　　　　　　　　　　 |30min|

👀 Allow the children to explore their skills in filling and emptying containers, using the water trays or large bowls of water, or working with the sand. It may prove easier to allow some part of the class to do this activity while the others complete the Copymaster, and then swop about.

👤 Ask the children to complete **Copymaster 59**, where they can demonstrate their understanding of 'full' and 'empty'.

Closing the lesson 　　　　　　　 |10min|

▦ Using children to act out the parts, invent a story called 'The Magic Milk Jug' or read the story of 'The Magic Porridge Pot' to the children

Assessment

Child performance	Teacher action
Reluctant to explore containers by filling and emptying them	Give the children practice over several sessions, of filling and emptying containers
Needs to practice the skills involved in carefully filling containers	Give the children practice, with adult supervision, so that they can take care, pour slowly and exactly fill containers
Can explore these concepts with care and confidence	Move on to the next lesson

Lesson 2 　　　　　　　　　　　　 ②

Key questions

Does this container hold more than this one?

Which of these two containers hold more/less?

Which of these three containers holds most/least?

Vocabulary

Fill, full, empty, pour, more, less, most, least, container

Introduction 　　　　　　　　　　 |10min|

▦ Using one of the water trays and some containers, discuss the idea that each container will hold an amount of water. Compare containers and talk about which holds more or less (two containers) or which holds most or least (three or more containers). Allow individual children to make some comparisons too.

Activities 　　　　　　　　　　　　 |30min|

👀 Set out some challenges on the board, drawing pictures of the containers that are available to the children. The challenges may look like the following.

Which holds more?

Which holds less?

Then allow the children to fill and compare the containers, using the water trays or large bowls of water, or working with the sand. It may prove easier to allow some part of the class to do this activity while the others complete the Copymaster, and then swop about.

👤 The children can show that they can make judgements about capacities on **Copymaster 60**.

Closing the lesson 　　　　　　　 |15min|

▦ Invite the children to either work in groups to draw a cartoon picture showing 'full', 'empty', 'more' and 'less' or make up a little drama involving characters like Mr Jug and Mr Beaker or Ms Water Butt and Ms Watering Can.

Assessment

Child performance	Teacher action
Finds it difficult to compare the capacity of a range of containers	With individual help and participation give the child practical comparison exercises using containers and water. Then repeat the activities found in Lessons 1 and 2

Can compare capacities, but needs more practice	Repeat the practical activity found in this lesson, over several sessions
Understands and demonstrates capacity comparisons	Move on to the next lesson

Lesson 3 ③

Key questions

How many … fill one … ?

Vocabulary

Fill, full, empty, pour, more, less, most, least, container

Introduction 10min

 Using a small container like an eggcup, tablespoon or doll's cup, show the children how they can measure how many of this small container filled with water will go into a series of larger containers like a plastic cup, a bowl and a jug.

Activities 30min

Write up a set of challenges on the board. They may look something like this:

Estimate ~
How many do you think?   How many **do** fill?

 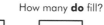

fill

fill

fill

Using your 'unit', how many fill?

Invite the children to complete the series of challenges, using the 'unit' that is set for their group and the water or sand tray, or bowl of water, along with a range of containers. If there is time, ask each group to allow every child a go at filling each container so that their results can be compared.

Ask the children to do the puzzles on **Copymaster 61**.

Closing the lesson 15min

Show the children how full the various pans are when holding all the portions of cabbage, or baked beans required for each day's school dinners or food for a party.

Assessment

Child performance	Teacher action
Struggles to use non-standard measures of capacity	Give the children plenty of supervised practical experience of activities like those in the lessons in this theme
Can use non-standard measures but needs more practice in order to fully understand.	Give the children more sessions like Lesson 3
Understands and uses non-standard measures	Move on to another theme

HOMEWORK

Send a note home asking if the children may try out some capacity experiments there. There are some suggestions on **Copymaster 62**.

Introducing time and timing

Learning targets

The children should be able to:

1 ➤➤ Use vocabulary of time and sequence events

2 ➤➤ Show they know about the calendar

3 ➤➤ Do simple timing

Before you start

Subject knowledge

There are three uses of time that children need to learn about. These are historical time, time taken, and time telling. The first of these is about chronology. This will lead to historical time-lines and similar activities but in the early stages we need to work on such events as birthdays and holidays. Time taken is about measuring the duration of an event. Typically young children will experience this sort of time in journeys, lesson length, doing something in a given time, and races against each other. Telling the time is about using clocks, watches and calendars. Time ideas should be built upon the life experiences of young children. The emphasis in lesson 2 is on the days of the week. Another similar lesson or lessons can be set up so that the children can learn more about the months of the year.

Previous knowledge required

An understanding that events like those in everyday life have an order, know what a timetable is, use some words related to time and timing.

Resources needed for Lesson 1

Flashcards with everyday words relating to time on them, for example, before, after, now, next. Educational catalogues, other catalogues and magazines depicting children doing a range of activities. Sugar paper, scissors and glue. Copymaster 63

Resources needed for Lesson 2

Flashcards with the names of the months and days on them. Old calendars, Copymasters 64 and 65

Resources needed for Lesson 3

Copymaster 66. Equipment necessary for each group to make a timer. This includes plastic bottles, sharp knife (for adult use only), water, sand, beakers, skewer or tapestry needle (for adult use only), stands to hold the timers (these can be made by cutting a hole in one end of a shoe box as shown on Copymaster 66). Extra adult help for this lesson would be invaluable.

Homework: Copymaster 67

Teaching the lessons

Lesson 1 ①

Key questions

What happened first?

What comes next?

What shall we put before this?

Can you put these in time order?

Vocabulary

before, after, now, next, early, earlier. earliest, late, later, latest, time 'taken'

Introduction 〔10min〕

▨ Talk to the children about their own experiences of time in the context of their daily routine, and the events of a school day. Use some of the vocabulary from the vocabulary list in the discussion.

Activities 〔40min〕

👥 Ask the children to find and cut out a picture of children working or playing. They should cut these out and stick them onto sugar paper. The pictures can all be pinned to a temporary board ready for use later in the lesson.

👤 Invite the children to number the pictures on **Copymaster 63** in order.

▨ Show the children the flashcards with everyday words relating to time on them, including those under Vocabulary opposite. Ask a row of children to stand at the front and invite the children looking on to call out a word at a time so that the child holding the word can step forward. Go through all the words two or three times.

Then invite the children to look at the pictures they have cut out in the first activity. With their help, make two sequences of about seven pictures, using words like 'next', 'before' and 'after'. Thus the children in the pictures can be doing seven different things in an order.

Closing the lesson ⬚10 min
▦ Look at Copymaster 63 again with the children and talk about the order of events.

Assessment

Child performance	Teacher action
Finds it hard to use the vocabulary of time and to sequence events	Give the children plenty of opportunities to talk, both in a one-to-one with an adult and in group settings, about the events of the day and ordering and sequencing in time
Can sequence events but needs to work on everyday vocabulary	Give the children the opportunity to work with the flashcards and master the vocabulary before moving on
Has an extensive vocabulary and can order events	Move on to the next lesson

Lesson 2 ②

Key questions
What day was it yesterday?

What day is it the day after tomorrow?

On what days do we come to school?

What month is it now?

Can you name the months in the year?

In what month is your birthday?

Vocabulary
yesterday, today, tomorrow, week, names of weekdays, month, names of months

Introduction ⬚10 min
▦ Write on the board the names of the days of the week. Invite the children to read them aloud. Give them quick-fire questions like 'What day is today?' 'What day is tomorrow?', 'What was the day before yesterday?' Then ask the children to recall one thing they did yesterday; on Saturday; that they will do tomorrow, and so on.

Activities ⬚35 min
👤 Give the children **Copymaster 64** and ask them to record in writing or pictures what they do on different days of the week.

▦ Draw up a typical calendar chart for one month on the board. Describe it to the children so that they can interpret it. Ask them questions about it.

👥 Give each group a page from an old calendar and ask them, as a group, to record the answers to the challenges on **Copymaster 65**.

Closing the lesson ⬚10 min
▦ Use the flashcards with the names of the days of the week on them. Ask children to hold them. Place the children in order. Read them out with the children.

Pin them up so that they can use them in their written work.

Assessment

Child performance	Teacher action
Does not know about the calendar	Begin by teaching the children to name the days of the week. Then invite the children to copy the words for the days, read the words for the days and look for the days on calendars. This should happen over a number of sessions. Then the children can repeat the activities set out in this lesson
Not yet confident about concepts to do with calendars	Take a few minutes out of several sessions to point out the features of the calendar, the days of the week and the date. Then return to some of the activities in this lesson
Understands and uses calendar facts	Move on to the next lesson

Lesson 3 ③

Key questions
How many times did you ... while the sand/water ran through?

Vocabulary
Timing, timer, count

Introduction ⬚10 min
▦ Explain that it is important for us sometimes to measure how long it takes to do a job, run a race, cook the tea and so on. And we also want to know how many times something can happen while a certain amount of time passes. Show the children what you mean by announcing that you think they can step from one foot to the other 20 times while you count to 10. Try it out. Try out some other timing exercises using arbitrary units, like taps made by a stick.

Activities ⬚40 min
👥 In their groups ask the children to make a timer, following the ideas presented on **Copymaster 66**. Then the children can undertake an activity and see if they can do it before a volume of water or sand has trickled through the timer. Example activities include the following:

- reading the page of a book
- writing their name and address
- completing a jigsaw or other puzzle activity
- working out 10 maths calculations.

Closing the lesson ⬚10 min
▦ Remind the children that we do sometimes need to

know what time has passed while something happens and we call this the 'time taken'. Ask the children to think of all the occasions they can, where timing is important. Examples may include athletics, swimming, music, school tests.

Assessment

Child performance
Finds it difficult to do simple timing

Understands what timing is but requires more practice

Understands and can do simple timing

Teacher action
Give the children tasks over several sessions, that can be completed in a short time; for example, 'Can you turn around before I clap my hands 3 times?' 'Can you jump six times while I count to 10?' Then talk about the idea of timing and repeat the activities done in this lesson

Over several short sessions give the children a range of timing challenges

Move on to a discussion of timing using standard units

HOMEWORK

Ask the children to draw a picture chart showing some of the things that happen in each month of the year. Give the children a set of timing puzzles including those on **Copymaster 67**.

Standard measures of length and introducing area

Learning targets

The children should be able to:

1 ➡→ Measure in metres
2 ➡→ Measure in centimetres
3 ➡→ Show they know what we mean by area

Before you start

Subject knowledge

Length and area are linked here because of the relationship between lengths of plane surfaces. In measuring a table top using hand spans, for example, the children can measure in at least two directions and will be informally aware of the fact that the table has a 'size' which is related to its length and breadth. Measuring lengths is a key skill as it is related not only to area but also in other measuring activities. When we read a scale on a measuring jug, temperature on a thermometer, and the pointer on a spring balance, concepts of linear measurement are required.

Previous knowledge required

What we mean by 'length', 'height' and other similar measuring words, experience of practical measuring using non-standard units

Resources needed for Lesson 1

Metre sticks, enough for one between two. Height chart to fix to a door jamb or the wall. Copymaster 68

Resources needed for Lesson 2

30cm rules (enough for one each for the children). A box of ribbons, yarns and short lengths of string (enough for one for each workgroup). PVA or fabric glue with spreaders and sugar paper. Coloured paper strips. Copymaster 69

Resources needed for Lesson 3

Small table and several tablecloths of varying sizes. Tea tray and tray cloths. Thin card to make face masks. Copymasters 70 and 71

Teaching the lessons

Lesson 1 ①

Key questions

How many metres long do you think this is? What is your actual measure of the length?

Vocabulary

Measure, metre, long, length, height

Introduction | 10min |

Remind the children of the work they have done when measuring length using non-standard measures. Discuss with the children the problems met when non-standard measures are used. Show them a metre stick and tell them that this a metre long, and a metre is an international standard measure, that is the same anywhere in the world. Ask the children to spread their arms to the length they think a metre is. Point to some things around the room and ask the children to estimate whether they think they are longer than a metre, or shorter than a metre.

Activities | 40min |

Allow the children to make estimates of the lengths of some of the things in the room, and then check with their metre sticks. For example, they may say the skipping rope is 1 metre and a bit, and measure it to find it is 2 metres. The children can all make a record of their work on **Copymaster 68**.

Using a home-made height chart to fix to a door jamb or the wall, measure the height of each of the children in turn. Mark in their heights and make careful comparisons between the heights of the children and one metre. For example, if you say, 'Trevor, the 1 metre mark comes in line with your nose,' this will give Trevor and his classmates a way of visualising the size of 1 metre.

Closing the lesson | 10min |

Tell the children that the metre is not the only standard unit, and we choose units and tools according to what we wish to measure. Show the children a metre measuring tape and discuss with them the kinds of things that might be easier to measure with the tape than with a metre stick. Show them the metre stick again and point out that they need to check whether the 'scale' of marks on the stick start at the very end or a little way in from the end. Point out that the metre may be marked off in smaller measures. These smaller measures are called centimetres.

Assessment

Child performance	Teacher action
Has not grasped the idea of measuring in metres	Give the children adult support and supervision in using a metre stick to measure things around the school. While the children are doing this, discuss what is happening and why we need to measure things. Then repeat the activities in this lesson
Can measure in metres but requires more practice	Give the children more challenges which involve using a metre stick
Understands the idea of standard measures and uses the metre with care and accuracy	Move on to the next lesson

Lesson 2 ②

Key questions

How long is this?

Do you think this is longer than 20 cm?

How long is your rule?

Vocabulary

Measure, centimetre, rule, long, length, height, cm

Introduction

Remind the children of what they have learned about standard measures of length and their work in measuring metres. Hold up a centimetre rule, and a metre stick and show that a metre can be marked off into 100 equal bits, each of which is a centimetre. The classroom rule commonly measures 30 centimetres. Show the children how the rule can be used to measure the lengths of things, and the importance of placing the start of the scale at the point at which one wishes to begin measuring.

Activities

Give each group a box of ribbons, yarns and short lengths of string and invite each child in the group to try some measuring using 30cm rules.

Allow the children to cut some coloured paper strips of a set range of lengths and glue them onto sugar paper. The outcome may look something like the following diagram.

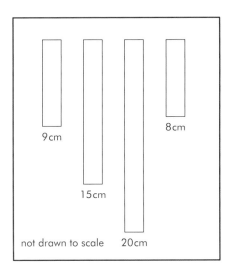

9cm

15cm

8cm

20cm

not drawn to scale

Ask the children to try the measuring tasks on **Copymaster 69**.

Closing the lesson   5min

Ask the children to estimate the lengths of the fingers of a volunteer classmate. Measure the fingers so that they can check their estimates. Then allow them to measure their own fingers.

Assessment

Child performance	Teacher action
Finds it problematic to measure in centimetres	Give the children individual support in measuring exercises, beginning again with non-standard measures if this is appropriate
Can measure in cm but needs more practice	Allow the children to repeat activities like those in this lesson
Careful and competent in measuring in centimetres	Move on to the next lesson

Lesson 3 ③

Key questions

If I tell you about the area of this, what exactly am I looking at?

Can you show me what we measure when we talk about the area of a room?

Vocabulary

Area, cover, length, breadth, width

Introduction   10min

Place the small table in front of the children and hold up in turn a number of pieces of material, only one of which exactly covers the top of the table. Try each out for size and show the children the one that 'fits'. Remind the children of their work on length. Point out that sometimes we want to measure not only how long something is, but also how wide it is (that is, its surface). When we make these measures we call them the area. Tell the children that the cloth that exactly matches the table top is the same area as the table top.

Now carry out the same activity allowing individual children to try a range of tray cloths on a tray. Find the one that matches in area.

Activities
35min

Working in pairs, so that they can help one another, invite the children to make a mask, using thin card, that exactly covers their face. There are some ideas for masks on **Copymaster 70**.

Invite the children to explore area by drawing their hand and counting squares on **Copymaster 71**.

Closing the lesson
5min

Choose some of the masks the children have made and ask them to try them on, and show the other children how they cover their face. Make a display of masks and hands cut from Copymaster 71.

Assessment

Child performance	Teacher action
Cannot show they know what we mean by area	With adult help and support talk about the

idea that we can measure 'what covers' and show the children examples like those in the lesson, and things like rugs, 'carpets of flowers', rainhats

Lacks confidence in work on area	Give the children more activities to do with the idea of 'coverage' and counting squares
Is confident and articulate about work on area	The learning targets for this theme have been met

HOMEWORK

Give the children some copies of **General Copymasters C** and **D** (large squares and centimetre squares). The children could then try drawing around some things like leaves and counting the squares to compare areas.

Standard measures of mass

Learning targets

The children should be able to:

1 ➤➤ Compare how much things weigh
2 ➤➤ Weigh in kilograms
3 ➤➤ Weigh in grams

Before you start

Subject knowledge

When we weigh things we actually measure their mass. Because 'weight' is the word we use in everyday speech, this has been used here. The use of standard measures is both a necessary step in the children's understanding and a regulated comparison. When we weigh an object and decide that it weighs, say, 125g then we are actually asserting that the object weighs the same as a particular standard weight. In other words we are comparing whatever we choose with given standard objects called weights or masses. This means that it is also important that the children eventually come to understand families of standard measures and their relationships, and can make sensible choices about which standard measures to employ in the light of issues about accuracy.

Previous knowledge required

What a balance is, how a balance works and non-standard measures of mass.

Resources needed for Lesson 1

Food packs with the mass of the contents displayed: these can include packets, cans and jars, and should have the full contents. Empty packaging from foodstuffs: this the children can collect ahead of the lesson. A one gram mass from a mass set. Copymaster 72

Resources needed for Lesson 2

Bathroom scales. A full kilo bag of flour and one of sugar. 10 mystery parcels each weighing a different amount, from 100g to 2 kilos or more. Copymaster 73

Resources needed for Lesson 3

Classroom balances on which to use sets of 1, 2, 5 and 10 gm weights. Small items from among classroom resources for the children to weigh. These should be assembled in matching sets for each work group. Copymaster 74

Teaching the lessons

Lesson 1 ①

Key questions

Which is lighter?
Which weighs more/most?
Can you find a pack with this weight written on it?

Vocabulary

light, lighter, lightest; heavy, heavier, heaviest; weigh less, least, more, most, weight

Introduction 5 min

Point out the numbers on some of the full food packs. Pass them around so that every child gets a close look. Write some of the numbers on the board, putting the 'g' after them. Tell the children that 'g' is short for grams, and this is a standard measure of how much something weighs. Place the packs in order putting the smallest number first. Allow individual children to lift the packs in turn, feeling the 'weight' of each.

Activities 30 min

Give each group five or six full food packs, that they can examine and lift. They can then make a group record of the 'weights' of the packages on a large sheet of paper, placing the lightest first.

Bring the class together and examine the rankings made by the groups.

Ask each child to choose an empty or full food pack from the array and make a drawing of it showing the actual 'weight' information on **Copymaster 72**.

Closing the lesson 5 min

Remind the children that the 'g' after the 'weight' is short for grams, and that a gram is a standard measure. Pass around a mass from the mass set that weighs one gram so that the children can see how small it is.

Assessment

Child performance	Teacher action
Cannot compare how much things weigh	Return to theme 19 and repeat those parts of the theme with which the children seem unfamiliar,

	before repeating the activities of this lesson
Compares things but finds ordering them difficult	Leave a display of full and empty packaging so that the children can look at the labels and access 'weights' by lifting up foodstuffs
Compares how much things weigh with confidence	Move on to the next lesson

Lesson 2 ②

Key questions

Do you think this weighs more than a kilo or less than a kilo?

How much do you think this weighs?

Vocabulary

Kilograms, kilo, weigh, 'weight', more than, less than, estimating, estimate

Introduction 5 min

 Show the children the full bag of flour and the bag of sugar. Point out that each weighs exactly one kilo, and that it says this on the packaging. Allow individual children to hold the bags to feel the 'weight'.

Activities 45 min

 Set up an 'estimating workshop' by placing 10 mystery parcels, numbered 1 to 10 and each weighing a different amount, around the room. Invite the children to all move around the room, estimating whether each parcel weighs more or less than a kilo. The full bag of sugar and of flour can be left out for the children to lift up and use as standards for comparison. the children can record their results on **Copymaster 73**.

Using the bathroom scales weigh each child and record how many kilos they weigh on a class chart.

Closing the lesson 5 min

Look again at the mystery parcels and tell the children which are lighter than and which are heavier than a kilo.

Assessment

Child performance	Teacher action
Does not understand about weighing in kilograms	Return to theme 19 and invite the child to weigh using non-standard measures before repeating work similar to that in this lesson
Needs more discussion and work before being confident with kilos	Repeat some of the activities of this lesson
Is ready for further challenges	Move on to the next lesson

Lesson 3 ③

Key questions

Can you find out what this weighs?

What is the sum of the 'weights' (masses) you have used?

Vocabulary

'Weight', weighs, balance, grams

Introduction 10 min

 Remind the children of the standard 'weight'– the kilo. Tell the children that there is a smaller 'weight' that is useful and that this is a gram. There are 1000 grams in a kilo. Using a classroom balance weigh something small. Demonstrate to the children the need for care in using a balance and how to judge which 'weights' (masses) may be appropriate to try on the scales. Allow a child to try weighing something else, while the class look on.

Activities 40 min

 Set the children some challenges involving weighing small things from around the classroom in grams. There should be a matching set of items for each workgroup. The children should each have the opportunity to use the classroom balances and sets of 1, 2, 5 and 10 gm weights.

Invite the children to complete the quiz on **Copymaster 74**.

Closing the lesson 5 min

Compare the results the groups got when weighing similar small items.

Assessment

Child performance	Teacher action
Is puzzled about weighing in grams	Return to theme 19, if necessary, introducing the children again to non-standard measures, before repeating the lessons in this theme
Can weigh in grams but needs more practice	Give the children more practical challenges, over several sessions, of weighing in grams
Confident in use of grams and in weighing accurately	The learning targets for this theme have been met

HOMEWORK

Ask the children to write down the 'weights' of the contents of one of the supermarket shopping bags. They can then sum the 'weights' (using a calculator if necessary) to see what a bag of shopping weighs.

69

Standard measures of capacity and volume

Learning targets

The children should be able to:

1 ➤➤ Discuss the volumes in which liquids are sold
2 ➤➤ Measure in litres and mls
3 ➤➤ Make estimates of volume and capacity

Before you start

Subject knowledge

Before introducing standard measures of capacity and volume we need to be sure that the children have had a good variety of practical experiences sustained over a period of time. A key skill in using standard measures of capacity and volume is the ability to read vertical scales accurately and consistently. There is also, of course, a need to appreciate that linear scales are actually being used to 'label' a three-dimensional characteristic. Only with this appreciation will children come to a genuine understanding of capacity and volume.

Previous knowledge required

Practical experience of filling and emptying containers using liquids and solids that 'pour' like sand, the use of non-standard measures.

Resources needed for Lesson 1

Empty containers of safe liquids such as washing up liquid, shampoo, cooking oil, fizzy drinks, squash, milk including individual and large sized cartons, plastic bottles and cans. Access to some of the children's lunch boxes (with parental permission)

Resources needed for Lesson 2

Litre jugs, measuring cubes and cylinders. Water trays or large bowls of water (one for each work group) and containers (for each work group):eggcups, beakers, jugs, bowls, patty tins, shallow dishes. Plastic aprons and sleeve protectors. Sand trays can also be used. Copymaster 75

Resources needed for Lesson 3

Resources as for Lesson 2. Copymaster 76

Homework: Copymaster 77

Teaching the lessons

Lesson 1 ①

Key questions

What does this container say on the side?

Do you think there was more in it than in this container?

Vocabulary

Container, full, empty, volume, liquid, l, mls

Introduction | 10 min |

▨ Show the children some empty liquid containers and draw them on the board, writing in the volume stated on the label. Compare the numbers and explain that a standard measure of liquids is a litre (l), and that a litre is made up of 1,000 millilitres (mls).

Activities | 40 min |

▣ Ask the children to examine at least five empty

containers, and write out what it says on the labels.

▨ Discuss the figures on the labels, determining which containers held more than others. Examine full drinks cartons in a number of the children's lunch boxes and make a class chart.

200ml	230ml	250ml
Lola's drink	Steve's drink	Tara's drink
Tim's drink	Asa's drink	Susan's drink

Closing the lesson | 5 min |

▨ Compare some of the containers the children looked at in their groups to determine which container held most, which least, which the same amounts.

Assessment

Child performance	Teacher action
Is confused about volumes and labelling	Give the children opportunities, over several sessions, to talk about the ideas of 'full' and volume, then recap on activities done in this lesson
Can talk about standard volumes but lacks confidence	Give more practice in activities like those in this lesson
Adept at declaring and comparing volumes	Move on to the next lesson

---

Lesson 2   ②

Key questions

How many mls fill the cup?

How many mls would you need for two drinks?

Where is the 1 litre mark on the jug?

Vocabulary

Container, full, empty, volume, liquid, mls, litre, millilitre

Introduction   10 min

Show the children a measuring jug with a 1 litre mark. Fill the jug to the mark with water. Tip the water in different containers in turn, asking the children each time what the volume of the water is. Then show the children a measuring cylinder and point out that using this we can measure out mls. Demonstrate how this measuring can be done.

Activities   40 min

Allow groups of children to fill and empty a range of containers with either water or sand, determining the volume of each container and recording it. The challenges can be written on the board, and half the class could do this activity while the other half work on the Copymaster, and then swop over.

Ask the children to try **Copymaster 75**.

Closing the lesson   5 min

Show the class again the conventions of writing down volumes, using the labels on drinks as examples.

Assessment

Child performance	Teacher action
Finds it hard to measure in litres and millilitres	Give the children adult support in discussing and measuring volume with non-standard and standard measures
Can measure volume but needs more practice	Allow the children more sessions of access to the water or sand trays and to calibrated containers. Set increasingly complex challenges until the children are confident

---

Accurately measures and records volumes	Move on to the next lesson

Lesson 3   ③

Key questions

What do you think the volume of this is?

How much will this container hold?

Vocabulary

Volume, capacity, litres, millilitres

Introduction   10 min

Remind the children that an estimate is not a guess. We can only make estimates when we are well-informed, and can make judgements on the basis of knowledge. Ask some children to estimate the volume of one of the containers in the water tray. Measure it carefully to see how close their estimates were. Point out to the children, the need for care in getting an accurate measure of liquid volume.

Activities   40 min

Ask the children to look at an array of containers including eggcups, beakers, jugs, bowls, patty tins and shallow containers. They should then draw six of them and estimate and write how much they think each will hold on **Copymaster 76**.

While the others look on, ask one child at a time to use water and a measuring cylinder to measure carefully the exact volume of the sample containers. The children can check these against their own estimates.

Closing the lesson   5 min

Check out with the children the names of the standard units for volume and how we write them.

Assessment

Child performance	Teacher action
Finds it difficult to make estimates of volume and capacity	Give the children copious practical experience of measuring volume so that they gain the knowledge to be able to estimate
Can estimate but needs more practice	Give the children more practice in activities like those in this lesson
Estimates with skill and accuracy	The learning targets for this theme have been met

---

HOMEWORK

Give the children **Copymaster 77** which asks them to find appropriate measures in a range of settings.

Telling the time

Learning targets

The children should be able to:

1 ➡→ Tell the time to the nearest hour
2 ➡→ Tell the time in half or quarter hours
3 ➡→ Tell the time including minutes and use the 24 hour clock

Before you start

Subject knowledge

Telling the time is one of the three key ideas about time, the others being an appreciation of chronology and historical time, and duration of an event. The skill of telling the time using a 12 hour clock or watch is closely related to other mathematical ideas such as the number line, fractions and angles and rotations. Later on the children will come to the 24 hour clock and the use of digital clocks and watches where there is a need to understand what the numerals mean and the fact that they are not decimal numbers even though they can look like this. Note that Lesson 2 relates to the teaching of 'half past'. The lesson can be modified using the same elements so that the children are taught to identify 'a quarter past' and 'a quarter to' the hour.

Previous knowledge required

Know some of the words we use in talking about time, for example, soon, yesterday, before, after; know what we mean by past, present and future, and timing.

Resources needed for Lesson 1

A large clock face with Arabic numerals. Display of clocks and space for clock challenges. Copymasters 78 and 79

Resources needed for Lesson 2

A large clock face with Arabic numerals. Small card clock faces with hands that can be moved (enough for one for each pair of children in the class). Copymaster 80

Resources needed for Lesson 3

A large clock face with Arabic numerals (with the minutes marked in). A minute timer. Digital clock. Numeral flashcards to make up a mock digital display. Copymaster 81

Teaching the lessons

Lesson 1 ①

Key questions

What is the time?
What time does the clock say?
What 'o'clock' is it?

Vocabulary

Numbers one to twelve, o'clock, time, hour, clock

Introduction ⏱10 min

▨ Before the lesson, set up a display of clocks (they need not be clocks that work), with a display board behind them for some time challenges. Show the children the different clock faces and ask the children to look very carefully at them. Discuss why it is that we need to know 'the time' and how long things take. Pin up some time challenges for the children to think about during the day. These can be changed from day to day. There are some examples in the following diagram.

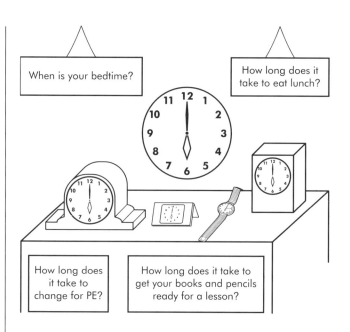

When is your bedtime?

How long does it take to eat lunch?

How long does it take to change for PE?

How long does it take to get your books and pencils ready for a lesson?

Activities ⏱40 min

▨ Show the children a large clock face with Arabic numerals. Point out the important features of the clock, using the vocabulary 'face', 'hands', 'numerals', 'hour'. Ask the children to close their eyes and imagine a large clock face. They can draw in the numerals with a 'magic' finger. Now show the children that the short hand is called the hour hand and it tells us what o'clock. When the long hand points to twelve it is 'o'clock' and the short hand will point exactly to a numeral, and that tells us what o'clock. Set the hands to show one o'clock. Then wind the long hand right around the face to point to twelve again and move the short hand to two. Say, it is two o'clock. Show the children how the long hand makes a journey right around the face while the hour hand moves from one numeral to the next. Set the clock to read… o'clock and ask the children what the time is. Do this several times.

👤 Ask the children to complete the o'clock puzzles on **Copymaster 78**.

▦ Talk to the children about what they are doing at every o'clock in the school day. Fill out a timetable picture chart on the board.

👤 Ask the children to draw pictures on their own timetable chart on **Copymaster 79**.

Closing the lesson   5min

▦ Remind the children that the hands go around the clock in the same direction as the numbers and that this is called 'clockwise'. Place the hour hand just before and just after the 'o'clock' and tell the children we can say 'it is nearly' or 'it is just past'. Set the hands close to a different 'o'clock' and ask the children to say whether it is 'nearly' or 'just past'.

Assessment

Child performance	Teacher action
Is beginning to learn 'o'clock but needs more practice at the initial steps	Give the children support in talking about clocks, time and 'o'clock'
Can tell o'clock but not confident with challenges when presented differently	Give the children more experience of challenges about 'o'clock'
Confidently tells the time on the hour	Move on to the next lesson

Lesson 2   ②

Key questions

What is the time?

What was the time a quarter of an hour ago?

What will the time be in half an hour?

Vocabulary

Time, hour, o'clock, half past, quarter past, quarter to

Introduction   10min

▦ Show the children the large clock face with Arabic numerals. Use pieces of card to show that the face can be cut into two halves.

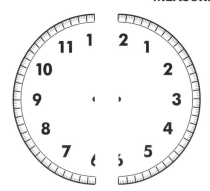

Show the children where the hands on the clock are when the clock says half past. Set the clock at half past two, half past three and so on, asking the children to give the time on the clock. Check that they understand that on the half hour the long hand is on the 6 and the hour hand is halfway between one numeral and the other.

Activities   35min

👥▦ Each child in the pairs should take turns at setting the hands on a small card clock face, in response to the teacher's challenges. These can include challenges such as:

- set your clock at half past six
- set the clock at half an hour before that
- set the clock at half an hour after half past two.

👤 Ask each child to complete **Copymaster 80**.

Closing the lesson   10min

▦ Work out with the children's help, what they are doing at every half hour during the school day.

Assessment

Child performance	Teacher action
Cannot tell the time in half hours	Use incidental opportunities to draw attention to the clock, give the children adult support in learning how we 'read' the time from the position of the hands, and then repeat the activities of this lesson
Can tell the time in half hours but not yet confident	Give the children more chances to practise this lesson's activities
Can tell the time	Move on to the next lesson

Lesson 3   ③

Key questions

What's the time?

What does this clock tell us?

How do you know it is morning/evening?

Vocabulary

Time, clock, digital display, o'clock, half past, quarter past, quarter to, minutes, 24 hour

Introduction 15min

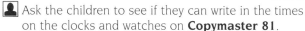 Use a large clock face with Arabic numerals (with the minutes marked in) to show the children that there are 60 minutes from o'clock to o'clock (that is one hour). Show them where the minutes are marked on the clock face. Set the clock at 20 past six, 4 minutes to twelve, 13 minutes to two and so on, asking the children what the time is for each example.

Now show the children a digital clock and match a time on the large clock face with a digital time. Allow volunteer children to set the clocks up to show some examples.

Activities 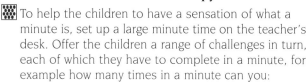 30min

 Ask the children to see if they can write in the times on the clocks and watches on **Copymaster 81**.

To help the children to have a sensation of what a minute is, set up a large minute time on the teacher's desk. Offer the children a range of challenges in turn, each of which they have to complete in a minute, for example how many times in a minute can you:

- say your name and address
- write your name
- blink your eyes
- hop on the same leg.

Closing the lesson 10min

Set up a flashcard display support as shown here:

Invite children to set out numeral flashcards to make up a mock digital display to match times you show on the large clock face.

Assessment

Child performance	Teacher action
Finds it difficult to tell the time including minutes and use the 24 hour clock	Rehearse again (several times each) the kinds of activities done in Lessons 1 and 2 in this theme. Then the ideas met in this lesson can be revisited
Can tell the time and use the 24 hour clock but needs more practice	Give the children more practice, particularly in working through word problems and challenges
Is confident and accurate in telling the time and using the 24 hour clock	The learning targets for this theme have been met

HOMEWORK

Give the children some time challenges. Here are some suggestions.

- Draw a timetable for one of your Saturdays.
- Draw pictures of all the clock faces in your house.
- Make up a rhyme to show you know what a second, minute, and hour are.

Shape and measure charts

Learning targets

The children should be able to:

1 ➡➤ Record shape and measure data
2 ➡➤ Interpret and draw block graphs
3 ➡➤ Interpret and draw tables

Before you start

Subject knowledge

Measures are centrally important to ideas about collecting, handling and representing data. Indeed, some forms of pictorial representation are only commonly employed when a measure is involved. For example, most line graphs need to have 'Time' on the x-axis. Examples include temperature in different months, rainfall over time, and distance and time. So early use of measures and data-handling approaches in tandem will help lay strong and important foundations for future understanding.

Previous knowledge required

Vocabulary and knowledge of shapes and measures as required in the lessons that follow, some recording skills (for example, tallying)

Resources needed for Lesson 1

A box containing about 20 toys. Large sheets of rough paper. Boxes of construction toys (for example, Lego®, Lasy®, Centicubes®). A box of 10 different ribbons and strings for each work group. Copymaster 82. A bowl of at least five different fruits

Resources needed for Lesson 2

A box of 10 mixed 2-D shapes, General Copymaster C, Copymaster 83

Resources needed for Lesson 3

General Copymaster C, Copymaster 84

Teaching the lessons

Lesson 1 ①

Key questions

Can you show what you have been doing on this piece of paper?

Can you draw what you have done?

Vocabulary

Record, tally, chart, information, data

Introduction 10min

▨ Tell the children that we can make special records or number pictures of the work we do. These pictures are important because they make it easy to get information and to understand what the numbers mean. Place the box of toys on the desk. Ask a child to take the toys from the box, one at a time and show how a tally chart can be made of the number of toys in the box. Tell the children that this number picture tells us quickly how many toys there are.

Activities 40min

▨ Give each pair of children a large sheet of rough paper and ask them to go around the room making a tally of all the rectangles and squares (or other appropriate shapes) they see. After a few minutes call the class back together and talk about the tally charts they have been making.

▨ Give each group a box of construction toys. Ask them to decide on a way of ordering these (it may be size, shape, number, colour) and allow each child in the group to make a record of the sort the group has made. Discuss the records with the children.

▨ Give each group a box of 10 different ribbons and strings and invite the children to make a record telling us about the ribbons and strings on **Copymaster 82**. They can all make a different kind of record if they wish, for example, a tally of colours or a Venn or Carroll diagram of sizes.

Closing the lesson 5min

▨ Show the children the bowl of fruit and talk about the shapes found there. Make a record of the shape contents of the bowl on the board.

Assessment

Child performance	Teacher action
Finds it hard to record shape and measure data	Allow the children to make a record of all maths 'play' activities, using whatever marks on the paper they wish, including tallies and pictures. Give them an opportunity to discuss these records. Then move on to the work in this lesson again
Can make a record of their work but needs	Give the children opportunities to make their own

more opportunities to practise a range of recording

Can record shape and measure data in a range of ways

records of all their work in subsequent shape and measure sessions. Move on to the next lesson when this is appropriate

Move on to the next lesson

Lesson 2 ②

Key questions

What does this mean?

Where should we put this information on the picture?

Vocabulary

Information, data, block graph, chart

Introduction 〔15min〕

On the board draw a grid. Using the box of shapes, take one out at a time and ask where it might go on the chart. The results may look something like this:

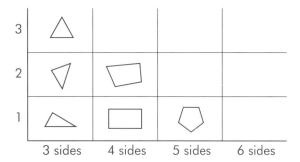

Tell the children that this sort of mathematical picture is called a block graph. Ask individual children questions like 'How many shapes with four sides are there? Point to the number that shows how many triangles there are.'

Activities 〔35min〕

Give the children copies of **Copymaster 83** and ask them to see if they can solve the puzzles together. They should then each make their own record.

Call the class together and work out the puzzles on the Copymaster. Ask the children additional questions using this same data.

Write up some data on the board for each child to put on their own block graph, for example some

information about children's lunch boxes and bags.

Ask the children to enter the data on a copy of **General Copymaster C**.

Closing the lesson 〔5min〕

Review the block graphs the children have made, and ask quick-fire questions enabling them to show they can further interpret their chart.

Assessment

Child performance	Teacher action
Cannot interpret and draw block graphs	Return to work like that set out in Lesson 1 in this theme
Can work with block graphs but lacks confidence	Give the children more chance to practice making and using block graphs
Readily interprets and draws block graphs	Move on to the next lesson

Lesson 3 ③

Key questions

Can you tell me about the information here?

Where on the table does it say...?

Vocabulary

Chart, table, information, data

Introduction 〔10min〕

Show the children what we mean by a 'table' in mathematics by using examples from newspapers and magazines. Draw a time 'table' of your day on the board.

Activities 〔35min〕

Invite the children to copy the teacher timetable, or draw one for their pet, onto a copy of **General Copymaster C**.

Ask the children to tackle the challenge on **Copymaster 84**.

Closing the lesson 〔10min〕

Make a table on the board using some data from the children themselves; for example, list the names of girls with long hair (shoulders or beyond), girls with short hair, boys with long hair, boys with short hair.

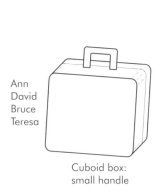

Ann
David
Bruce
Teresa

Cuboid box: small handle

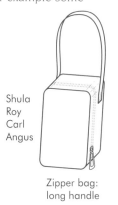

Shula
Roy
Carl
Angus

Zipper bag: long handle

Paul
John
Linda
Gill
Sue
Pat

Backpack: buckles, shoulder handles

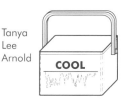

Tanya
Lee
Arnold

COOL

Small cool bag: long handle

Assessment

Child performance	Teacher action
Cannot interpret and draw tables	Give the children individual support in doing work relating to tables, lists and recording maths data
Can work with tables but needs more practice	Over many sessions give the children more chances to practise making and using tables
Confident in working with tables	The learning targets for this theme have been met

HOMEWORK

Give the children General Copymaster C and some plain paper. They will then be able to practise making charts, using their toys or other information in the home and from the family.

Investigations

- Using a strip of wood and paints or marker pens, ask the children to make a ruler measuring in hand-spans, thumbs or fingers.
- Make a collection of shoes or gloves and use them to make measurements. They can be given names like 'Cinderella's Slipper' and 'The Giant's Boot'.
- Make a collection of different shaped containers. Work out a way of finding out when they are half full and mark this point on each container.
- Ask a grown up in your home which items of shopping are hardest to carry. Tell the teacher and classmates what these are and why you think they are hard to carry.

Assessment

- Make comparisons between two objects.
- Compare three objects in relation to a measure.
- Measure given things using non-standard and then standard measures.
- Say what a range of measuring tools are used for.
- Say what standard measures would be used in a range of situations.
- Make a table of some given measurements.

Copy these words.

| shape | corner |

shape

| face | edge |

| flat | curved |

Cut out  . Learn the words.

Match the shape

Join and colour matching shapes.

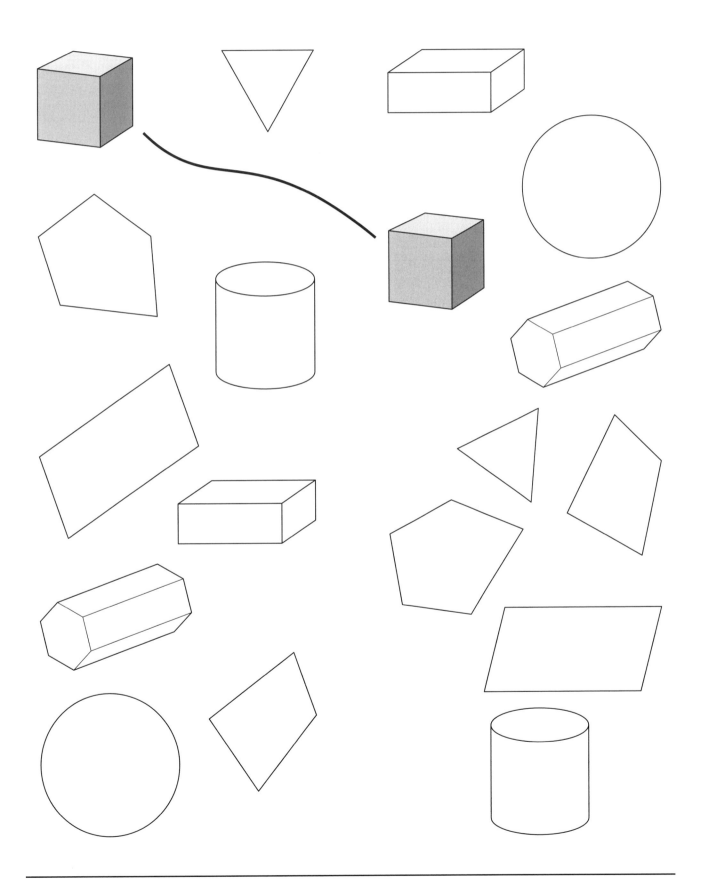

Sets of shapes

Colour each set of shapes in a different colour.

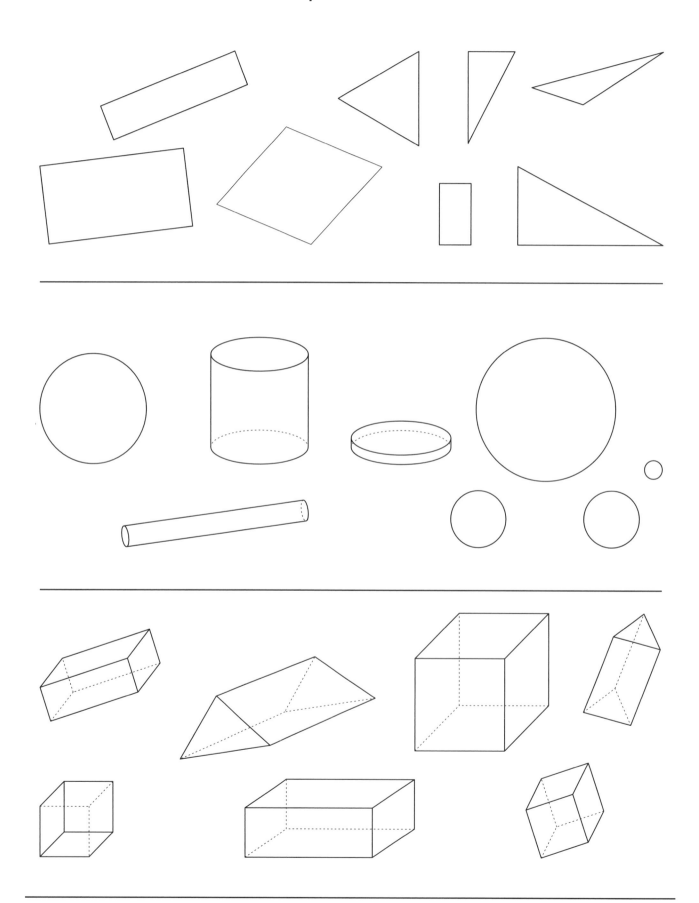

Shape	Where I saw this shape (write or draw).
Draw another shape here.	

Natural and manufactured shapes

Draw the things you would put on your displays.
Show as many different shapes as you can.

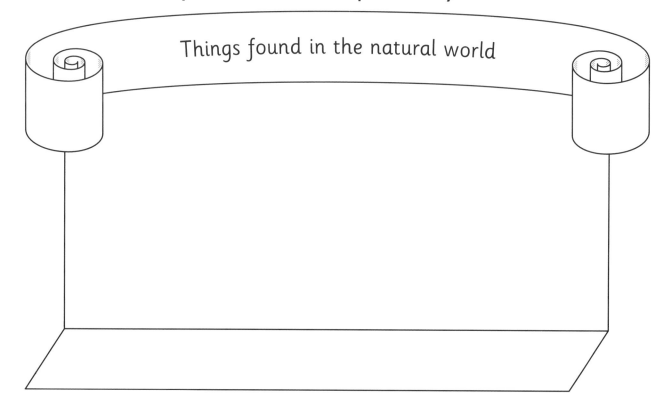

Things found in the natural world

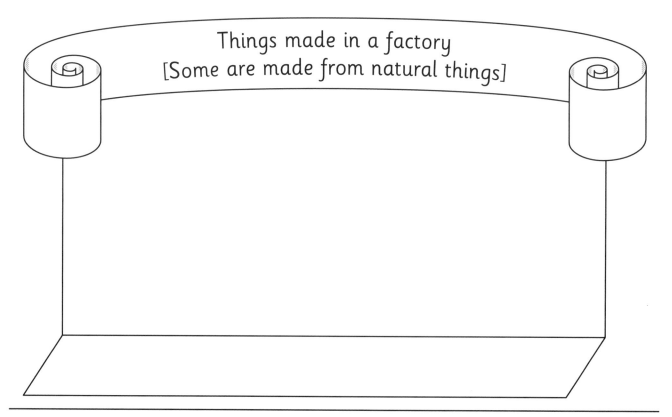

Things made in a factory
[Some are made from natural things]

Naming 3-D shapes

Colour cuboids red, cubes blue, triangular prisms black and cylinders green.

Feelie bag quiz

What's my name?
Write the names of the shapes in the feelie bag.
The cuboid has been named for you.

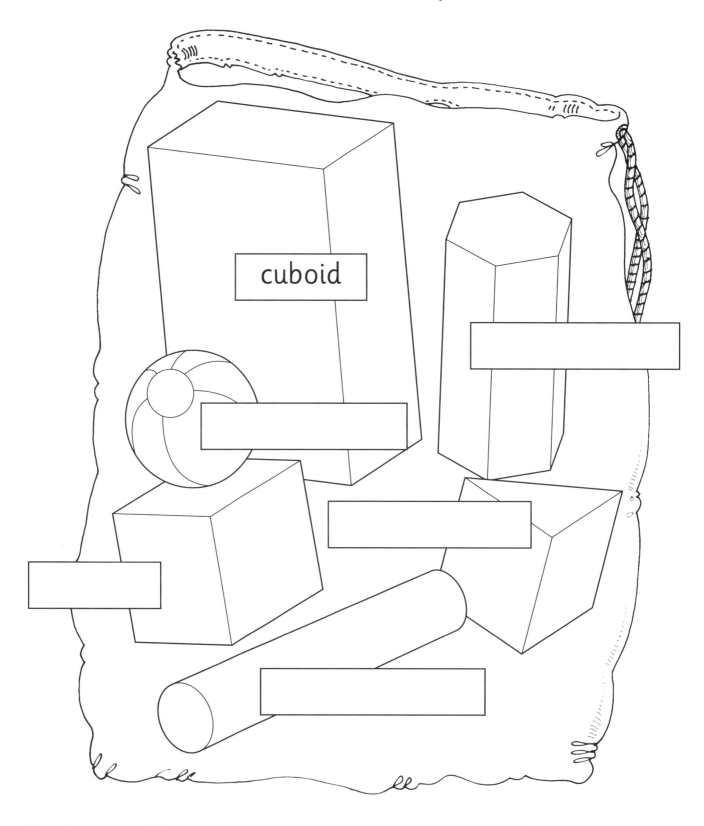

cuboid

84

Cubes and cuboids

Which of these are cubes? Which are cuboids?
Which are neither cubes nor cuboids?

Write **cube**, **cuboid** or **neither**.

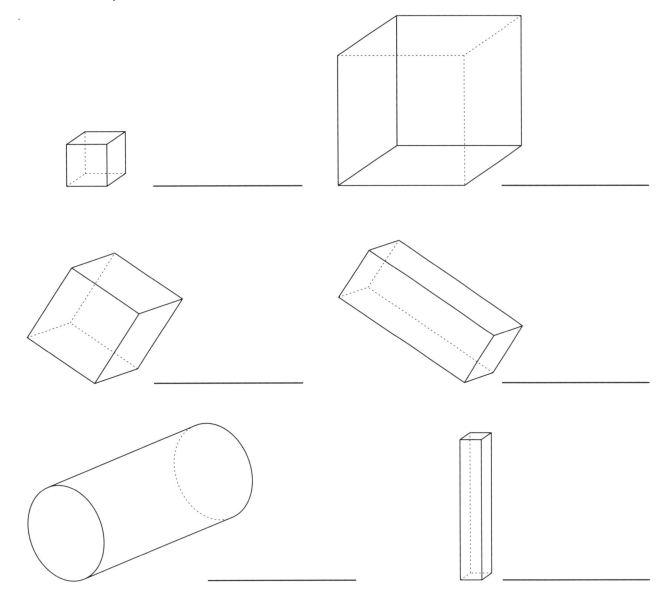

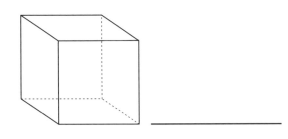

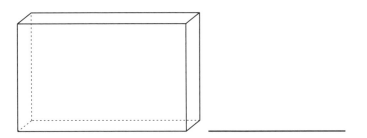

What I need to know about cuboids

What do you know about cuboids?

Write down the things that are the same about all cuboids.

What can you say about faces?

What do you know about their corners?

Write what you know about their edges?

Which of these are nets of the cube?
Colour the correct ones green.

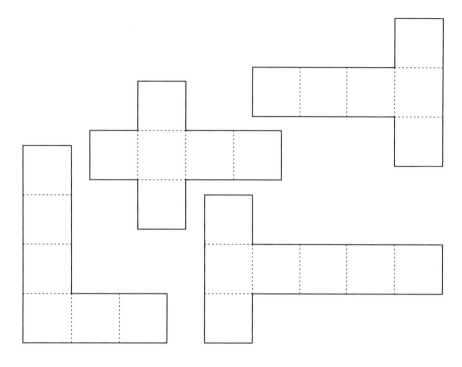

Two of these are nets of the cuboid.
Find them and colour them red.

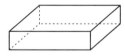

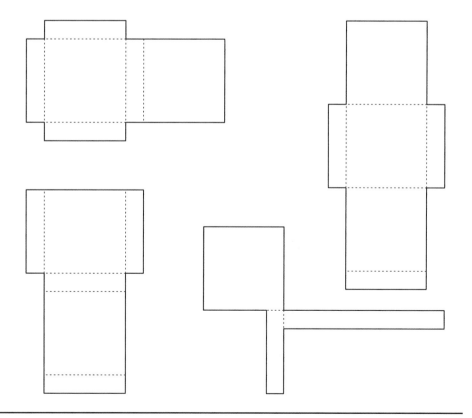

Net cards

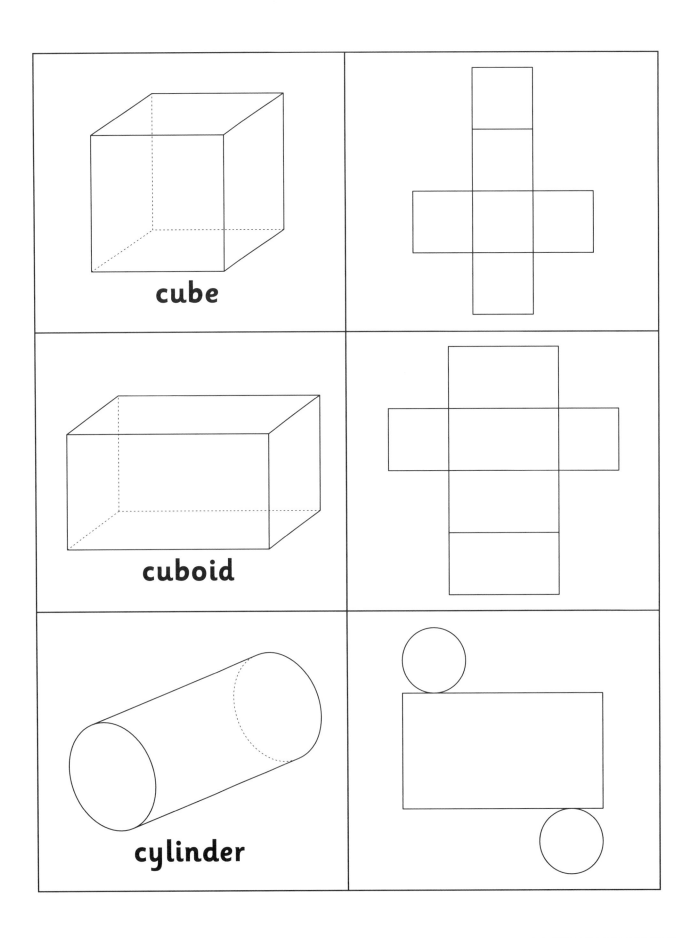

cube

cuboid

cylinder

Label the <u>cylinders</u>.

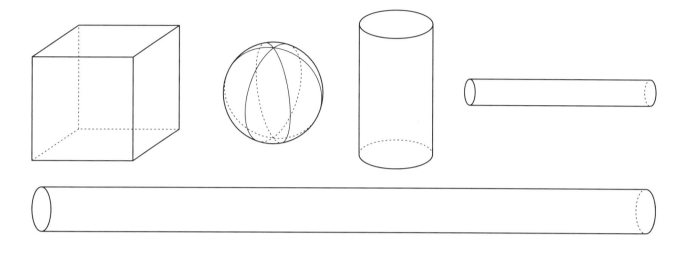

Colour the cylinders green.

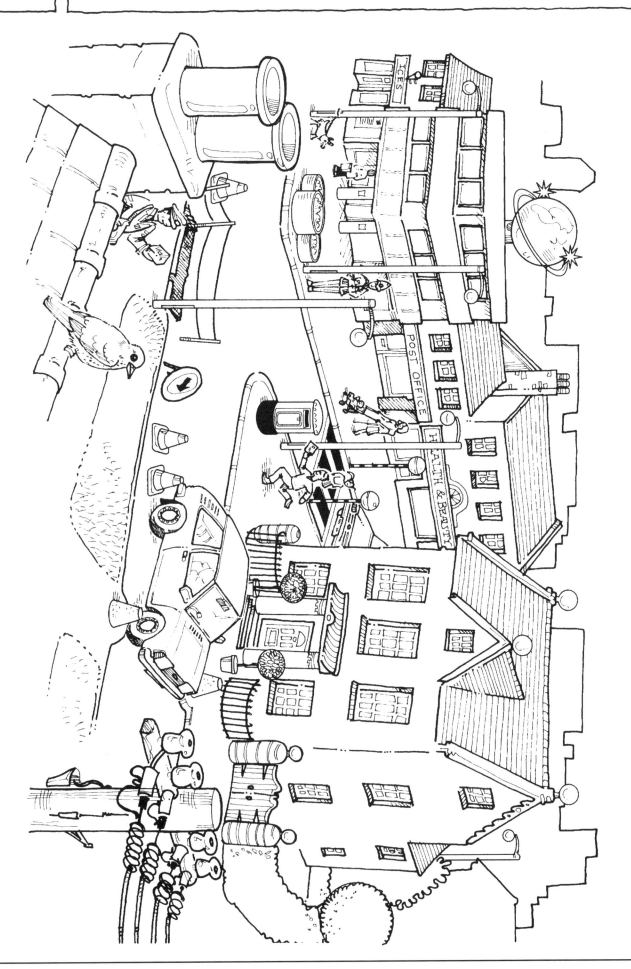

13 | Name the shapes

Join the labels to the diagram.

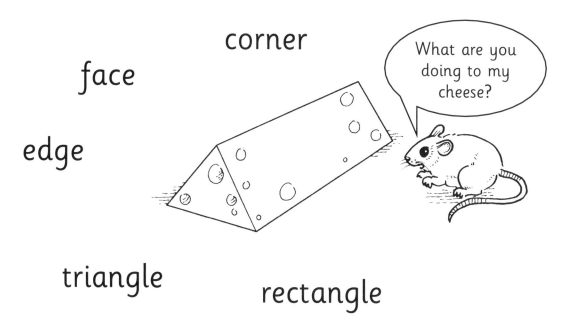

corner

face

edge

What are you doing to my cheese?

triangle

rectangle

Tick (✔) which are true, cross (✘) which are false.

A triangular prism has 5 faces.

A triangular prism is a flat shape.

A triangular prism has 3 rectangular faces.

A triangular prism has 2 triangular faces.

A triangular prism has 9 edges.

A triangular prism has 6 corners.

Here are 3 shapes. Colour the prisms.

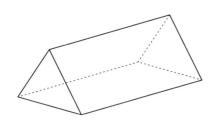
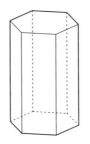
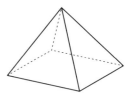

What is the other shape called? _____

Can you spot their nets? Join each shape to its net.

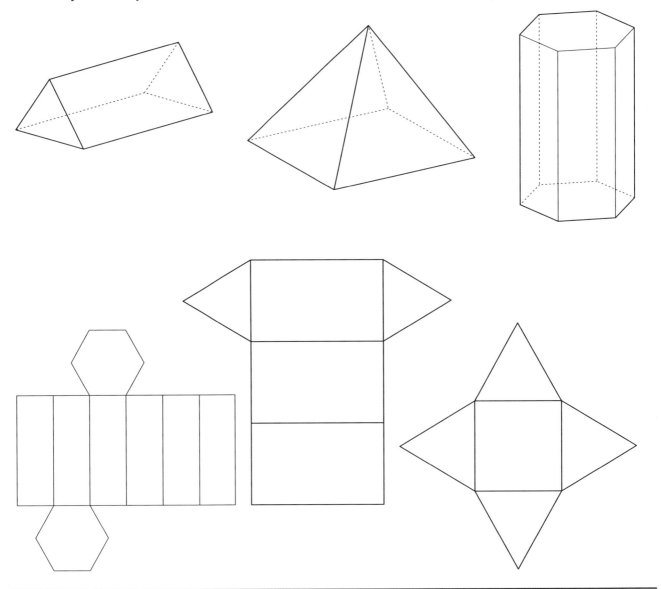

16 Prism and pyramid puzzles

Can you make a pyramid from Lego® building bricks or boxes? Draw your pyramid here.

These boxes are shaped like triangular prisms. They have been stacked.

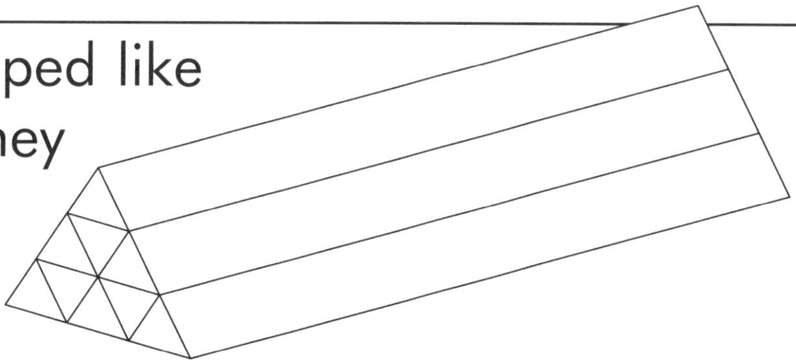

How many boxes are there?

☐ boxes

What shape is the stack?

____

Show your work to your teacher.

Talk or write about shapes in the classroom that match these shapes.

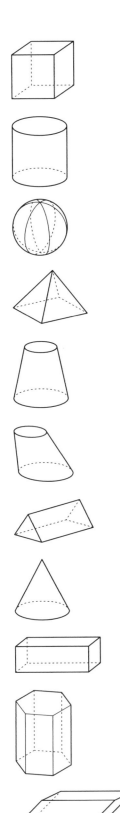

Testing 3-D shapes

Try out some tests on the shapes. Write or draw them in the chart here.

Test	Shape	What happened
Does it roll?		
Does it stack?		
Does it fit with other shapes like it?		

Why?

Why do cereals come in cuboid boxes?

Why is a milk carton cuboid?

Why is a ball a sphere?

Why are roofs prism-shaped?

Why not?

Why are wheels not cubes?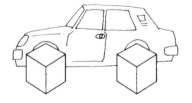

Why is a pyramid not a
good shape for a mug?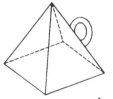

Why are dice not like cones?

 If 4 similar cuboids are stacked up what shape is made?

_____

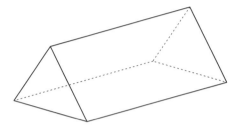 What shape is made when similar triangular prisms are stacked up?

_____

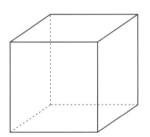 What two shapes could we make by pushing lots of cubes together?

_____ and _____

 What shape do two halves or hemispheres of an orange make?

_____

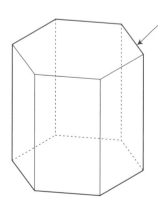 Why are boxes like this easier to pack than boxes like this?

_____

_____

_____

Use colours to show shapes that go together.

Draw lines to join each pair of matching shapes.

Talk about your work.

Can you make these shapes on your geoboard?

I have made a square on my geoboard.

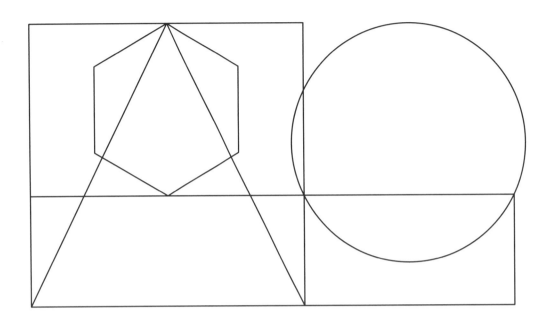

Trace these shapes with your finger in the maze above.

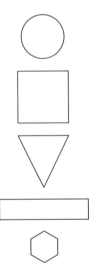

How many of these are there in the maze picture?

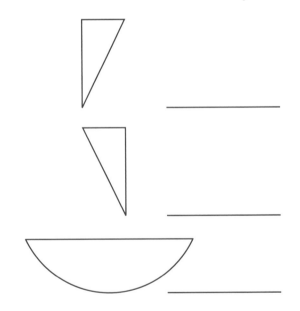

Draw a shape picture here.

Square and rectangles

Using two colours, colour a set of squares and a set of rectangles.

Draw and colour.

A set of green squares

A set of red rectangles

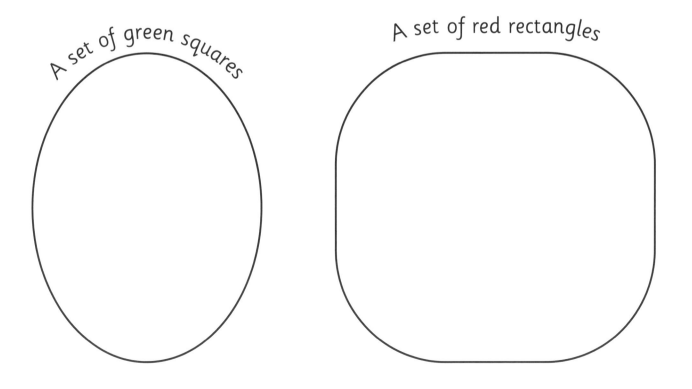

All about squares and rectangles

Write what you know.

All about squares.

All about rectangles.

Draw lines joining the shapes to their names.

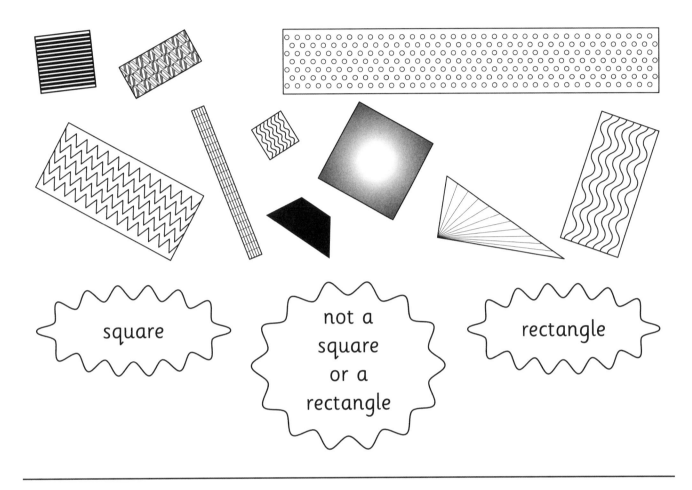

square

not a
square
or a
rectangle

rectangle

How many rectangles can you see here? _____

Are there 3, 4 or 5 squares? _____

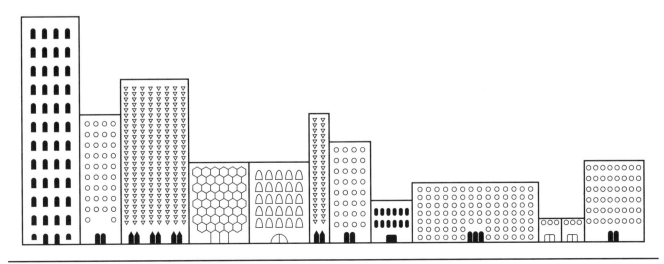

Make a set of circles

Colour the circles red. Colour all the other shapes yellow.

Looking for circles

Look for circles in the picture.

Name these shapes.

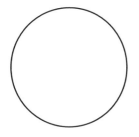 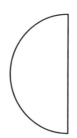

_____   _____   _____

How many circles can you make?

2 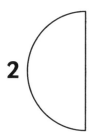   4   8   6

_____ whole   _____ whole   _____ whole   _____ whole
circle   circle   circles   circles

Wally the woodlouse is walking around these shapes.

When he walks around a
circle he is always the same
distance from the centre.

Colour the shapes that give Wally
a circular walk.

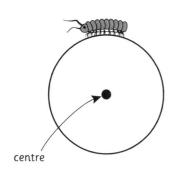

centre

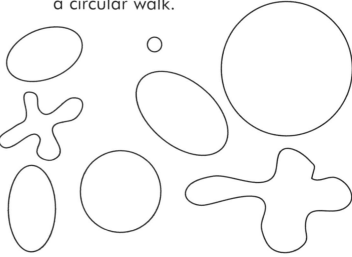

Make your own drawing aid

Cut a card ring from corrugated card.
Make it 6–10 cm across.

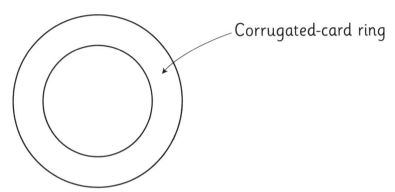

Corrugated-card ring

Now cut a small circle of the same card and make a hole in it for the tip of a ballpoint pen.

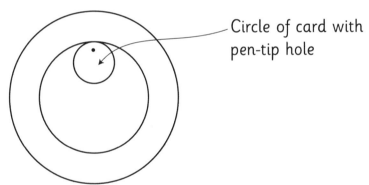

Circle of card with pen-tip hole

Try drawing patterns using your drawing aid.

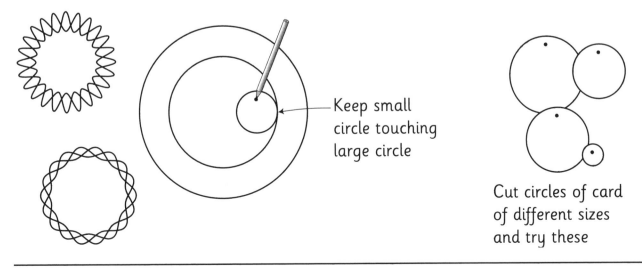

Keep small circle touching large circle

Cut circles of card of different sizes and try these

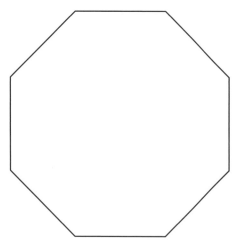

Draw lines to cut this shape into triangles.

If these triangles were pushed together what shapes would they make?

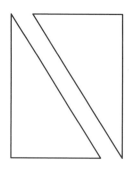 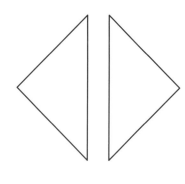

_____   _____

Draw the tumbling triangles that come next.

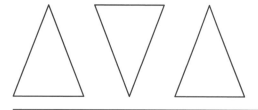

_____

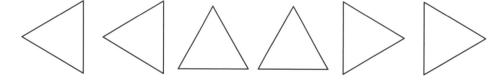

_____

_____

1, 2, 3, 4 ~ Join to make triangles.

1 · 4   · 3   . 2

2 ·   · 3   4.   .   .1
                             1   2   3   4

Hexagon patterns

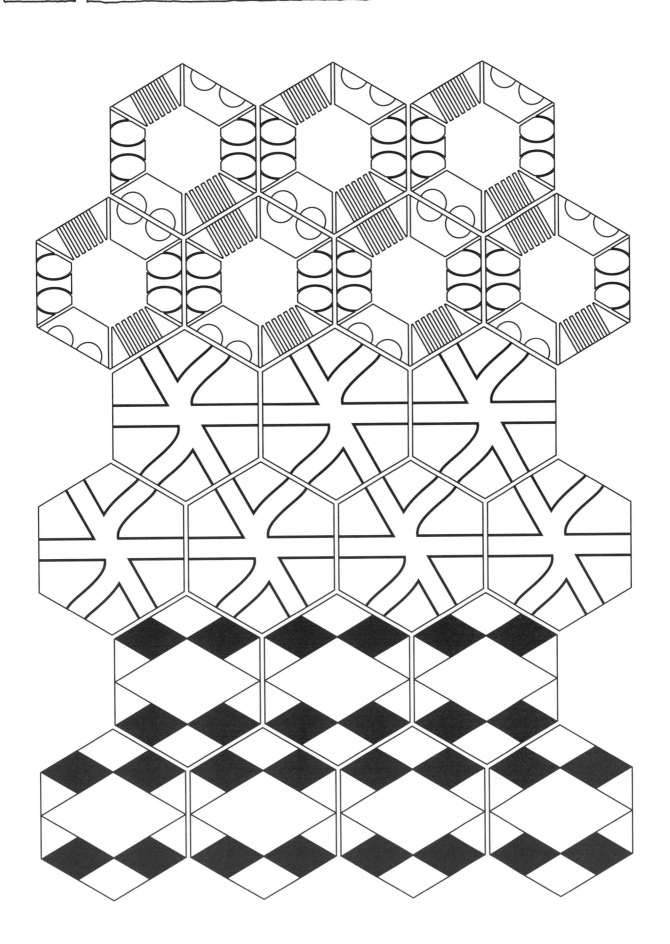

Patterns with 2-D shapes

Continue the patterns, then colour the shapes.

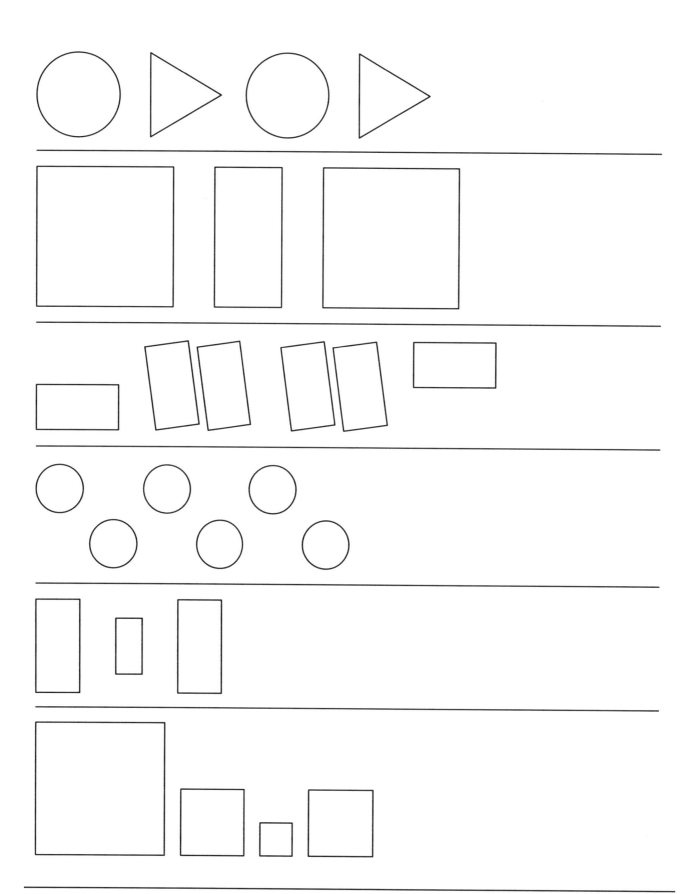

Cut out in card.

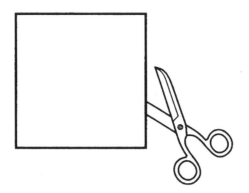

Cut a piece off one side

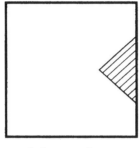 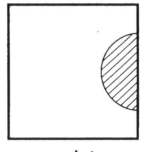

like this   or this.

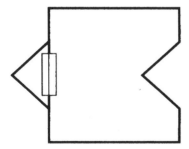 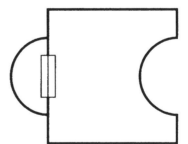

Stick it on the other side. Draw around the whole shape and make a tessellating pattern.

Can you see the halves?

Can you see the 'halves' of these pictures?
Draw a line to show the halves.

Reflections

Use a plane safety mirror to make reflections of these pictures. Draw what you see in the mirror.

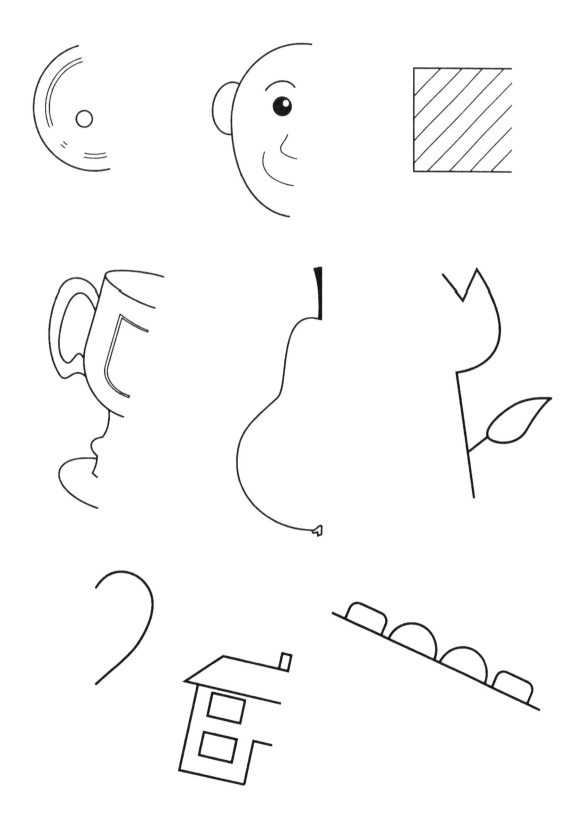

Draw in what you think the reflections will be. Then check with a plane safety mirror.

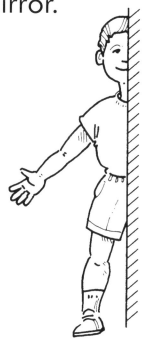

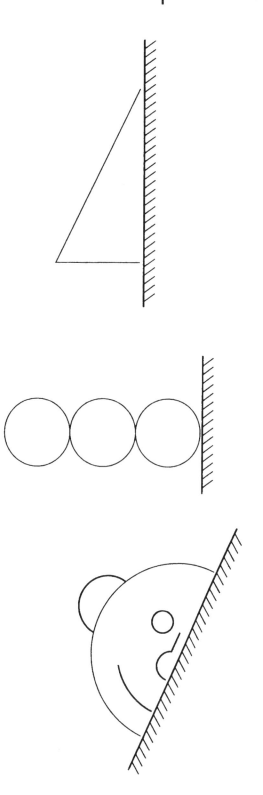

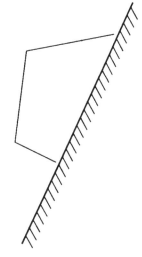

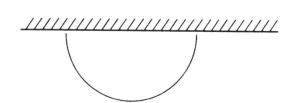

Colour your pictures.

Where are they?

Where is the custard pie?

Write **over**, **under**, **on**, **in**, **beside**, **behind**, **in front of**, or **next to**

_____

_____

_____

_____

_____

_____

_____

_____

Write **left** or **right** for Zoe.

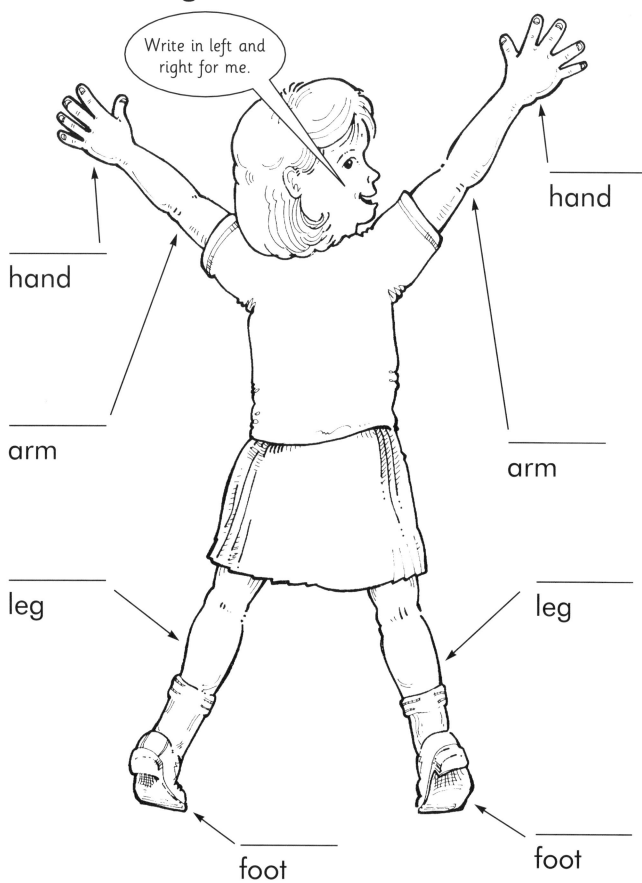

Write in left and right for me.

hand

hand

arm

arm

leg

leg

foot

foot

Find some routes through the maze.

Say when are you turning left.
Say when are you turning right.

Patterns with shapes

Continue the patterns.

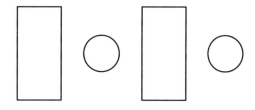

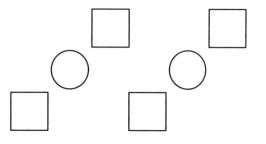

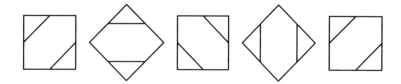

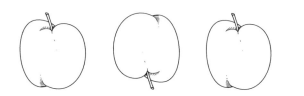

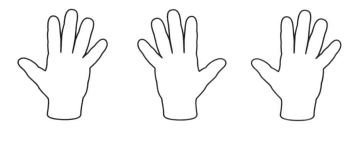

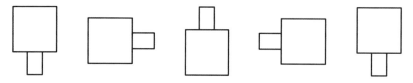

Draw and write a comic story.

Use **up**, **down** and other words like this.

Angles all around us

Mark all the angles you can find .

Mark in the right angles ⌐ like this.

All kinds of angles

Draw some of the angles you can see and label each one **right angle**, **less than** or **more than**.

1	2	3
4	5	6
7	8	9
10	11	12

Label the angles

For each angle write in **less than**, **more than** or **right angle**.

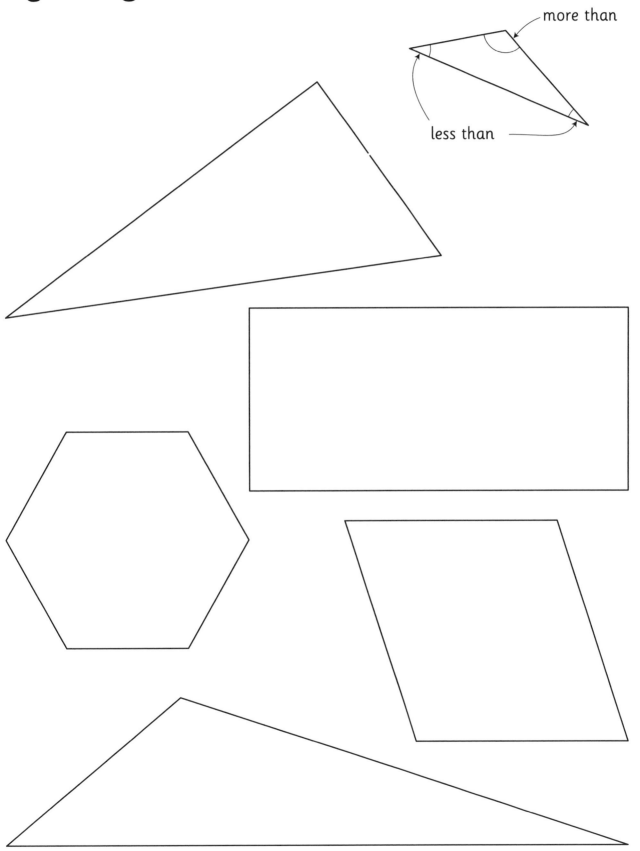

Open a door	Turn a page in a book
Close a cupboard	Open a plastic bottle
Open a pen	Close a window
Close a lunch box	Pick up a cup
Wind a ball of wool	Draw a circle
Wind up a toy	Row a boat
Draw a rainbow	Lock a door

Which way will it turn?

Draw in ↺ and ↻ to show the turns in each picture.

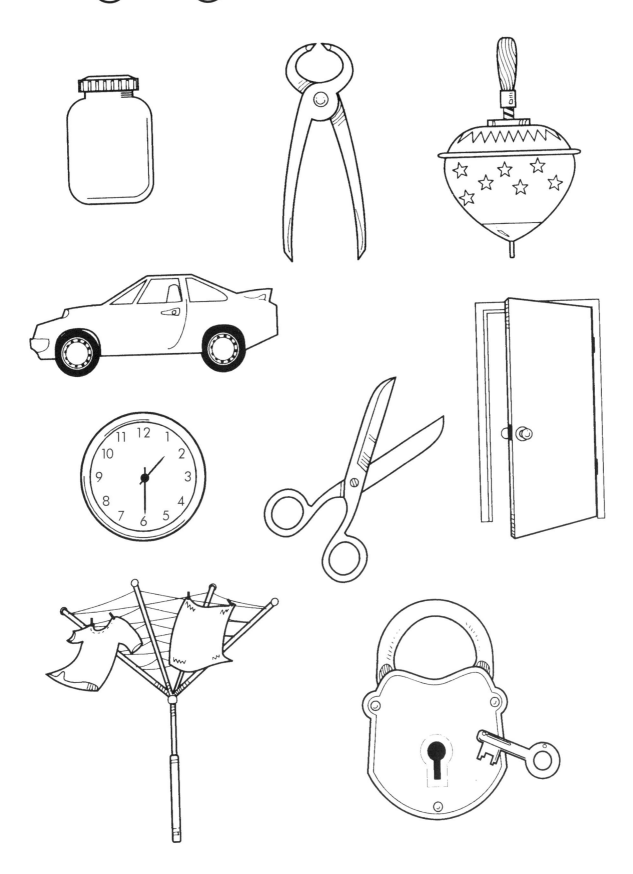

Patterns from turns

Draw around and cut out a card shape. Draw around it, then turn it and draw around it again. Repeat this over and over to make a pattern.

Drawing straight lines

Use a ruler. Complete the pictures

House

Robot Ross

Truck

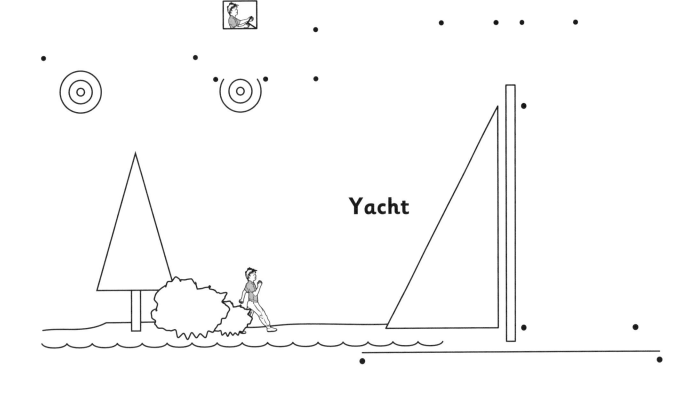

Yacht

long	longer	longest
short	shorter	shortest
tall	taller	tallest
wide	wider	widest
big	bigger	biggest
large	larger	largest
small	smaller	smallest
thin	thinner	thinnest
fat	fatter	fattest

Write in words to compare these.

_____ _____ _____

_____ _____ _____

_____ _____ _____

_____ _____ _____

_____ _____ _____

Ordering by size

Put these pictures in order of size, by numbering them

Measure	Use	How many?
a book	straws	
a door	hand spans	
a chair	hand spans	
a carpet	paces	
across a room	strides	
a pencil	thumbs	
a blackboard	hand spans	
a desk	pencils	

Fun measuring sticks

Make fun measuring sticks. Stick on card and cut out.

Which is lighter/heavier?

Tick the lighter (✓).

 or

 or

 or

 or

Put a cross by the heavier (✗).

 or

 or

 or

 or

Tick the lightest (✓).

 or or

 or  or

Put a cross by the heaviest (✗).

 or or

 or or

A record of my weighing work

Draw or write about your weighing work.

Draw or write here	**balanced with**	Draw or write here

Pick up things around the house. Find some that are really heavy and some that feel very light. Find two things lighter than a pencil.

Who is the heaviest in your family?

(name)

Which is the lightest of your pets or toys?

(name)

Compare some fruits from the fruit bowl or biscuits from the tin. Which sort are the lightest?

Which sort are the heaviest?

Is it full or empty?

Draw inside the containers to show they are <u>full</u>.

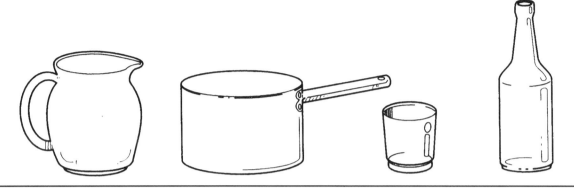

Draw these containers and show they are <u>empty</u>.

a glass   a jam jar

Write in **full** or **empty** under each container.

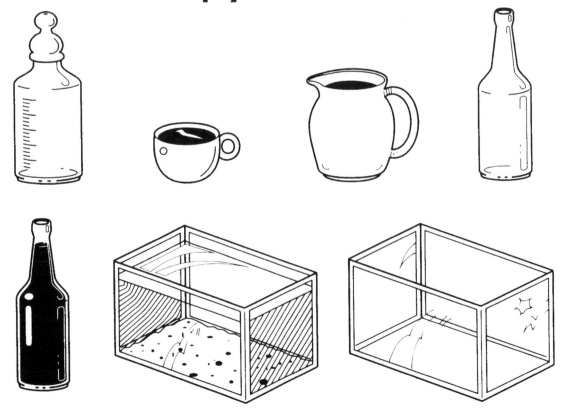

Which holds more?

Draw a ring around the object in each pair that holds more.

mixing bowl

teaspoon

swimming pool

water butt

cup

teapot

teaspoon

tablespoon

toy bucket

bucket

small drinks bottle

juice carton

Filling different containers

Draw your 'unit' here.

How many of your unit do you think will fill each container?

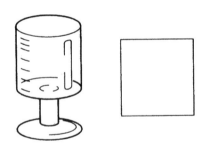 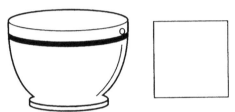

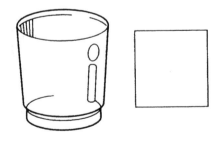 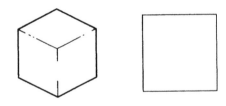

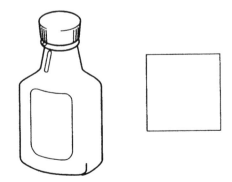

Capacity work to try at home

Ask the grown-ups at home whether you may work at the sink, with a bowl of warm water. Fill some containers with water. Compare them. Draw some of the things you filled.

This held most	This was hardest to fill
This was easiest to fill	This held least

My daily routine

My diary

Write or draw what you do each day.

Monday	
Tuesday	
Wednesday	
Thursday	
Friday	
Saturday	
Sunday	

Look at your calendar page.

Try to answer these questions.

What is the month on your calendar page?

What day of the week is the first day of the month?

How many Tuesdays are there?

What dates are the Fridays?

How many days are in your month?

Build your own timer

Sand clock

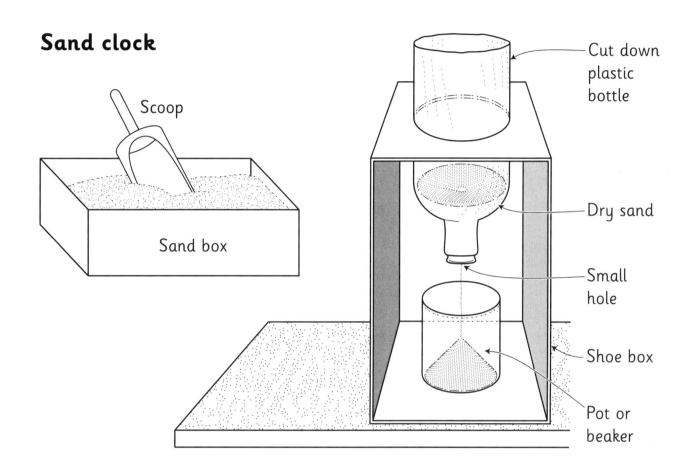

Scoop

Sand box

Cut down plastic bottle

Dry sand

Small hole

Shoe box

Pot or beaker

Water clock

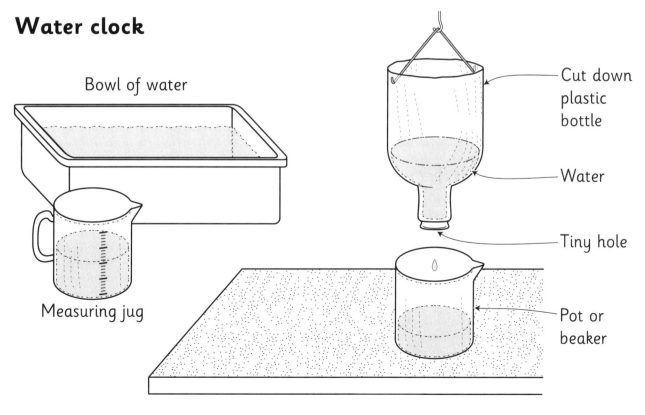

Bowl of water

Measuring jug

Cut down plastic bottle

Water

Tiny hole

Pot or beaker

See if you can draw or write the answers to these puzzles.

How many months of this year have passed?

How many months is it until your next birthday?

How many years ago were you 2 years old?

Write down about how many minutes, hours, days, weeks or months it takes to:

wash and dry the clothes

read a book

grow some seeds

get photos back from shop

draw a picture

fall asleep in bed

How long is it?

Draw what you are going to measure	Estimate what you think it measures	Write what it actually measures

145 Learning Targets: Shape, Space and Measures Key Stage 1

Measuring in cm

Measure each line. Write your answer on the line.

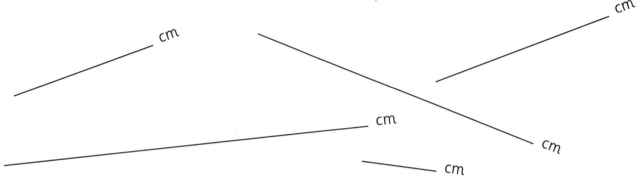

cm

cm

cm

cm

cm

cm

How long is each ribbon? Write your answer on the ribbon.

These worms are all 10cm long. Make their tails longer. Measure and draw it in carefully.

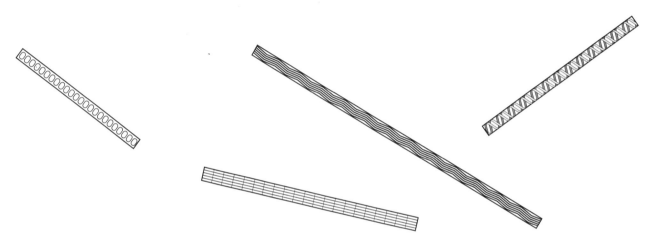

+ 3cm

+ 5cm

+ 4cm

146 Learning Targets: Shape, Space and Measures Key Stage 1

Ideas for masks

How big is your hand?

A teacher drew around her hand.
How many whole squares does her hand cover?
Only count the whole or nearly whole squares.

Draw your hand on top of hers.
How many whole squares does your hand cover?

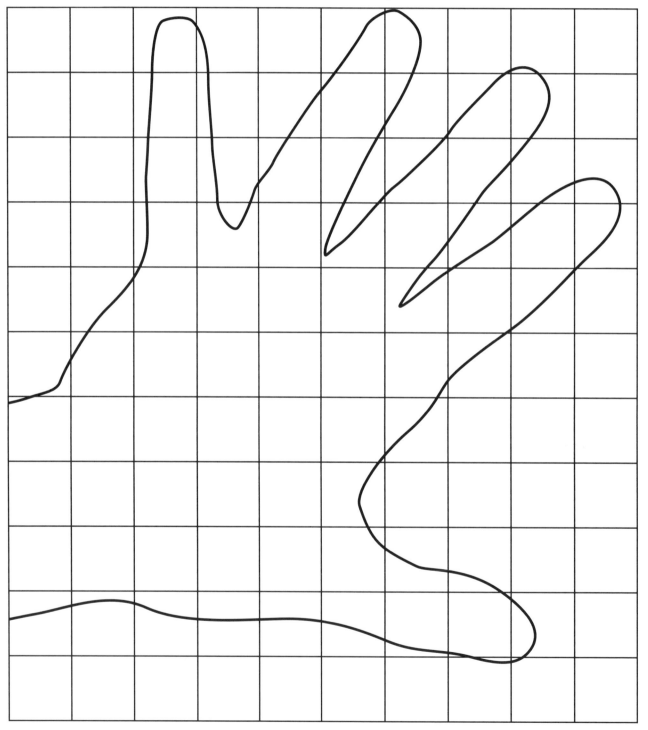

How much does it weigh?

Make a drawing of a food pack. What weight does it say it is?

Draw here. Make your drawing fill the page.

Is it more or less than a kilo?

Estimate what the mystery parcels weigh.

	More or less than 1 kilo?		More or less than 1 kilo?
1		**6**	
2		**7**	
3		**8**	
4		**9**	
5		**10**	

Lisa weighed the things in her pencil case.

pencil monster   pencil   paper clip   eraser

2g   10g   1g   5g

What are the 'weight' totals?

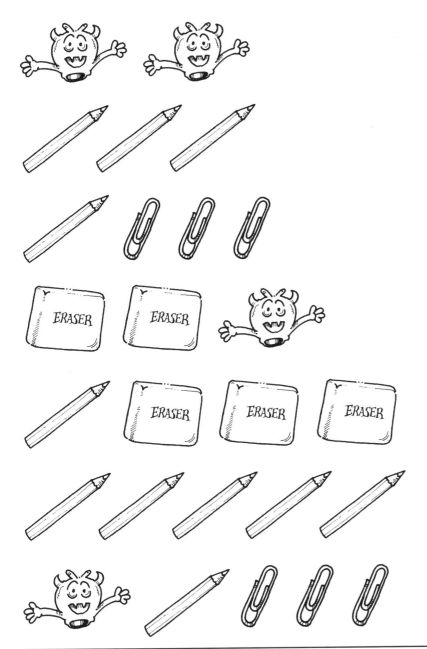

How much liquid?

Write in the volumes of liquid.

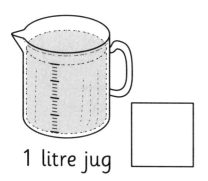

1 litre jug

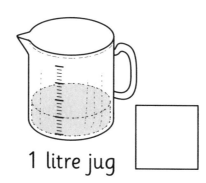

1 litre jug

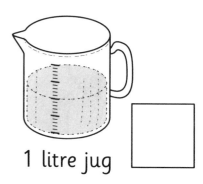

1 litre jug

5 cartons of juice = 100 mls. How much in each?

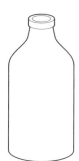

The milk makes 4 chocolate drinks.
How much in each cup?

1 milk bottle = 500 mls

1 litre jug

How many times can the small
glass be filled from the jug?

100 mls

How much does it hold?

Container	**My estimate** – how much I think it holds
Draw	Write

Which measure?

Join each picture to the measure that you think is correct. Look carefully first and use a different coloured pencil each time.

5 kilos

2 litres

1 m

  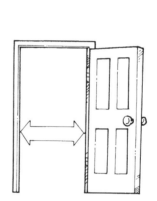

1 l

$2\frac{1}{2}$ litres

500 ml

The quantity of water to make tea for all three teachers.

40 cm

1 kg

$\frac{1}{2}$ kilo

50 cm

Put in the hands.

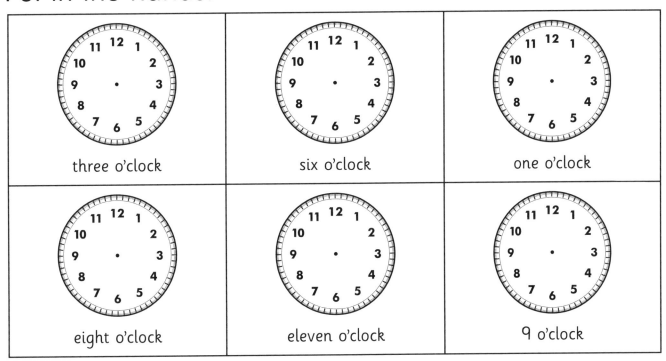

three o'clock

six o'clock

one o'clock

eight o'clock

eleven o'clock

9 o'clock

What is the time?

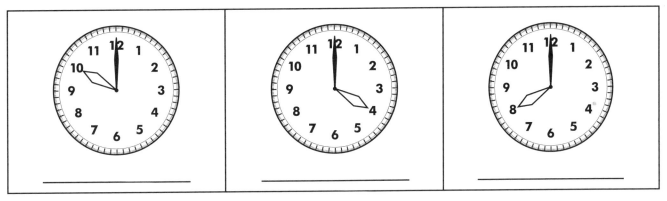

_____ _____ _____

The long hand is missing here. Draw in the hand and write the time.

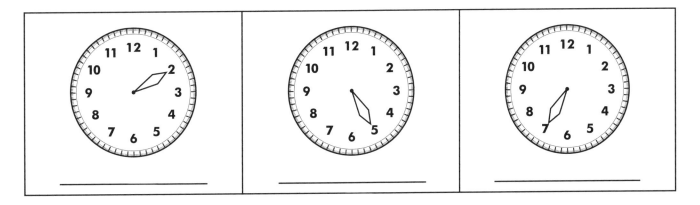

_____ _____ _____

My own timetable chart

What do you do each day at these times in school?
Draw and write

What time is it?

Put in the hands on the clocks.

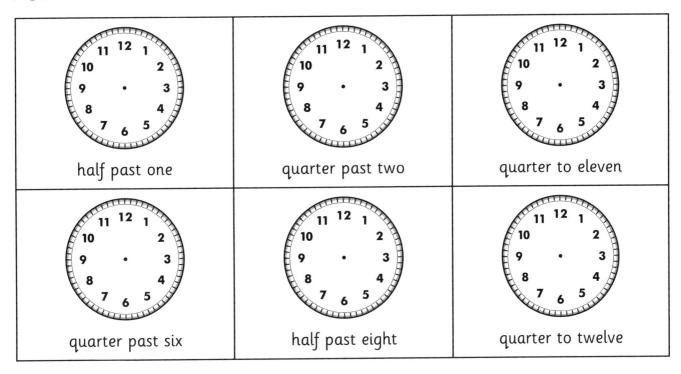

half past one

quarter past two

quarter to eleven

quarter past six

half past eight

quarter to twelve

What is the time? Write in what the clocks say.

_____   _____   _____

Write in times you choose. Draw the hands.

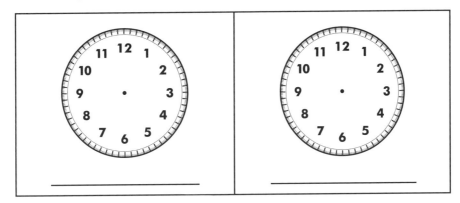

_____   _____

Clocks and watches

What is the time?

Recording data

Look in the box of ribbons and strings.
You may like to compare
lengths, thickness,
colour or possible uses.

Make a record
of what you find.

Children were asked to name their favourite ice cream.

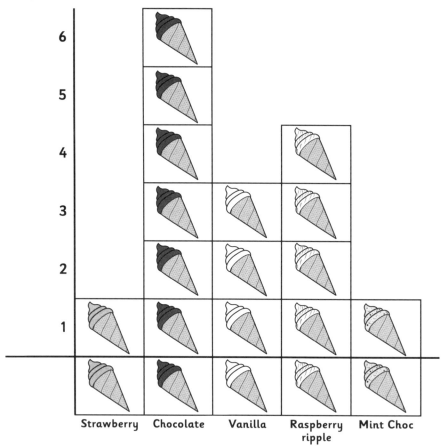

How many children chose strawberry?

Which ice cream is most popular?

Which two ice creams got the same number of votes?

_____   _____

How many votes did 'vanilla' get?

How many children voted?

Displaying information

Can you make a table of this information?
Work out the features of the shapes first.

triangle

pentagon

4 sides
4 corners

square

hexagon

rectangle

Make a table of all this information.

HAT SHOP

round hat
large brim

tall hat
small brim

tall hat
large brim

flat hat
large brim

round hat
small brim

flat hat
small brim

feather hat
small brim

feather hat
large brim

Dotty paper: squares

Dotty paper: triangles

Large squares

Small squares

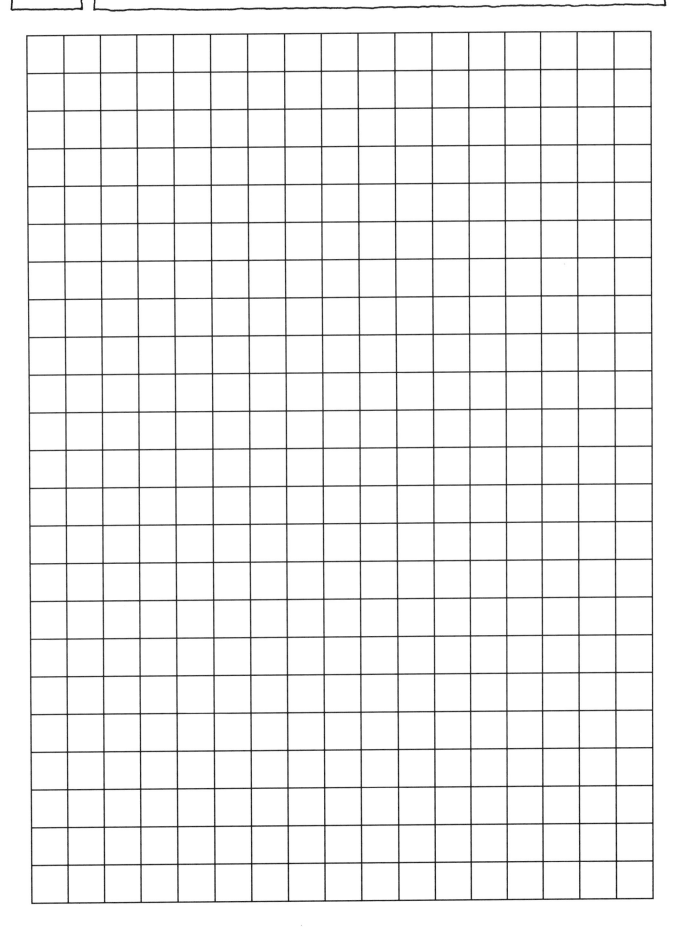

RECORD SHEET

Name _____ Class/Year _____ Teacher's initials _____

Section	Theme	Performance in relation to learning targets			Summative remarks
		1	2	3	
Introducing Shape	1 Vocabulary of shape				
	2 Matching and ordering				
3-D Shapes	3 Shapes around us				
	4 Cubes and cuboids				
	5 Cylinders, cones and spheres				
	6 Prisms and pyramids				
	7 All about 3-D shapes				
2-D Shapes	8 Flat shapes				
	9 Rectangles and squares				
	10 Circles				
	11 Triangles and hexagons				
	12 Patterns and tessellation				
	13 Reflective symmetry				
Position and Movement	14 Developing a vocabulary				
	15 Describing position and direction				
	16 Angles				
	17 Angle, movement and direction				
Measures and Data	18 Introducing length				
	19 Introducing mass				
	20 Introducing capacity and volume				
	21 Introducing time and timing				
	22 Standard measures of length and introducing area				
	23 Standard measures of mass				
	24 Standard measures of capacity and volume				
	25 Telling the time				
	26 Shape and measure charts				